7-14-61

2244

THE MOLECULAR BASIS

OF

EVOLUTION

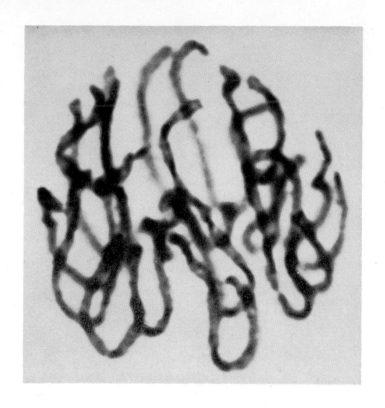

The
MOLECULAR BASIS

NEW YORK • JOHN WILEY & SONS, INC.

London • Chapman & Hall, Limited

OF EVOLUTION

CHRISTIAN B. ANFINSEN

National Heart Institute
National Institutes of Health
Bethesda, Maryland

TO MY MOTHER
AND
TO THE MEMORY OF
MY FATHER

PREFACE

The writing of this book has been stimulated by the excitement and promise of contemporary protein chemistry and genetics and by the possibilities of integration of these fields toward a greater understanding of the fundamental forces underlying the evolutionary process. It has become, inevitably, a highly personal volume expressing the experimental and philosophical outlook which has resulted from a process of self-education in an unfamiliar area of science. As with many biochemists, pure biology, including genetics, has not been a major exposure in my education, and the process of learning something about these subjects has been both a revelation and a struggle. Various kind, and frequently amused, friends, versed in the complexities of modern genetics, have sifted through these pages, and I hope that most of the misinterpretations and frank mistakes have been eliminated.

It has been highly interesting of late to observe how many scientists, working either in protein chemistry or in genetics, or for that matter in relatively unrelated fields, have arrived at long-range research plans that are similar to my own, down to almost the last detail of experimental planning. This book, therefore, will undoubtedly represent the point of view of numerous other biologically oriented individuals. On the other hand, some of the ideas to be discussed are so new and controversial that for every well-informed reader of this book who, in general, approves them there may be another who considers them nonsense.

The recent advances in the development of techniques for the study of protein structure have made it possible to elucidate the complete amino acid sequences of a number of rather large polypeptides possessing hormonal activity, and nearly complete sequences should soon be available for several with enzymatic activity as well. Concomitantly, there have been developed methods for the analysis of the finer, more subtle, structural aspects of proteins, concerned with folding, intramolecular bonds of various types, and intermolecular interactions. These advances now begin to enable us to discern the vague outlines of macromolecules, in the three-dimensional sense, and to ascribe their physical behavior and biological activity to specific covalent and noncovalent structural features.

We like to believe that Nature has been extremely wise and efficient in the design of the chemical compounds, however large and complicated, which make up the structure and machinery of living things. Thus, although chemical differences are found among the representatives of a given protein as isolated from a variety of species, we tend to suppose that such variations, rather than being fortuitous and unimportant irrelevancies, are part of a complicated and highly integrated set of variations in all the functionally and structurally important elements of the cell, the summation of which accounts for the unique morphology and phenotypic character of the individual organism.

In the last few years, a number of studies have shown that various biologically active molecules may be subjected to considerable degradation without loss of functional competency. It becomes necessary, therefore, to consider that the "macromoleculariness" of proteins and other large molecules may, in many cases, be concerned not only with a specific biological property but with other, more subtle, phenomena of cellular activity and engineering not yet apparent, such as adsorption to surfaces or substrates. We must, perhaps, expect a multiplicity of variables in the "natural selection" of variants in molecules, all of which may, together, determine the biological suitability of a particular molecular species.

An understanding of the underlying principles governing the species specific variations in molecular structure and of the effect of such variations on species characteristics must involve a clarification of the process of translating information present in the genetic material of the cell into the chemical language of enzymes, regulators, and the like. Such considerations are only now becoming possible as the result of the dramatic strides taken in the last few years in genetic theory and methodology, and a portion of the discussion in the following pages will have to do with the experimental background of the analysis of genetic fine structure and with the possible significance of such analysis to the question of protein biosynthesis.

It is abundantly clear that the metabolic organization of all living cells, whether plant or animal, shows a remarkable uniformity. Even a cursory examination of the literature of comparative biochemistry and physiology indicates that such biochemical functions as glycolysis, proteolysis, and fatty acid degradation, as well as more integrated processes such as electromotor activity and active transport through membranes, are ubiquitous in nature. Discounting the likelihood of completely parallel evolution in the plant and animal kingdoms, and in their major branches, we are led to conclude that, long before significant specialization, there existed in the waters of the earth various primeval forms of life which were endowed with representatives of most of, if not all, the important biological processes characterizing living things as we know them today. Although it is unlikely that we shall ever have more than opinions regarding the origin of life, it does seem possible to approach, experimentally, the nature of the *speciation* which began when such primeval cells had become established. This approach must involve a backward extrapolation of the information we can obtain on the chemical and genetic factors in organisms chosen from our modern environment.

Before examining for the reader the aspects of the mechanism of evolution that have been particularly illuminated by recent advances in biology and chemistry, it has been necessary to outline, in a broad sort of way, some of the basic fundamentals of evolution and the specific sciences, particularly genetics, that have contributed so essentially to its understanding. In the opening chapter, therefore, I have collected and rephrased some gleanings from the massive literature of morphological evolution to serve as a background for what follows. In several subsequent chapters is presented further preparatory material dealing with classical and contemporary genetics and with the basic facts of protein structure. Finally, after some discussion of the rapidly expanding body of knowledge relating structure to function in biological systems, I have considered a few aspects of natural selection in evolution which suggest themselves as a result of contemporary research, as well as some experimental approaches at the molecular level.

This book was written for pleasure, with the desire for self-enlightenment as the major stimulus. Since I cannot help but feel that everyone in science must be interested in the evolutionary process as the central theme of biology, I have listed a number of the original articles and books which contributed to the subject matter of this book.

I am greatly indebted to many of my friends and colleagues, including Dr. W. F. Harrington, Dr. Daniel Steinberg, Dr. W. R. Carroll, Dr. E. D. Korn, and Dr. W. D. Dreyer, who have read and helped improve various chapters of this book. I should also like to express my gratefulness to Dr. Bruce Ames for his patient help in connection with some of the discussions of genetic subjects. My special thanks are due Professor John T. Edsall of Harvard University and Dr. Michael Sela of the Weizmann Institute of Science, Rehovoth, Israel, who have read the entire manuscript and whose suggestions have been invaluable in the avoidance of error and in the improvement of style and organization. Finally, I should like to thank my wife, Florence Anfinsen, for the cheerful and understanding support she gave to a frequently rather morose husband.

CHRISTIAN B. ANFINSEN

Bethesda, Maryland
May 1959

GROUND RULES

FOR

THE READER

A prospectus of this book was circulated to a number of experts by the publisher before the actual job of writing was begun. The opinions received have been very helpful in establishing what I hope is the proper slant. One opinion, in particular, expressed a point of view so similar to my own that I have asked its author, Dr. William Stein, of the Rockefeller Institute for Medical Research, for permission to reproduce it here.

It has always seemed to me, and I may be wrong in this, that when an expert communicates with the relatively non-expert, he has a responsibility to stay pretty close to the facts. An expert can speculate to other experts without scruple. They have the equipment to meet him on his own grounds, evaluate the evidence and accept or reject the speculation as they choose. The non-expert has no such basis for evaluation. He has to accept relatively uncritically what the expert tells him, and hypothesis and fact soon become confused in his mind. A plausible speculation—and the speculations of the true expert are always plausible—can soon masquerade successfully as gospel. In the present state of our ignorance, I would regard this as unfortunate. It would seem to me that a book such as this one should aim to stimulate thought and experiment among practicing scientists, and should not lull the uninitiated into thinking that we understand more than we do.

We shall deal, in this book, with many contemporary hypotheses, some of which are far from general acceptance. Consequently, I would like to emphasize two points of caution to the reader. First, simple examples have purposely been chosen to illustrate the presentation of subjects which in fact are sometimes complicated by exceptions and inconsistencies. Second, it will be apparent that the author, like anyone else, has occasionally taken sides.

CONTENTS

chapter 1

THE TIME SCALE
AND SOME
EVOLUTIONARY PRINCIPLES

To most of us, paleontology is the name of a sort of genteel outdoor science concerned with the collection and gross description of old bones and hardened mud blocks containing preserved animal tracks. To the paleontologist and, for that matter, to any novice who has had the good fortune to pass through what might be called the "Darwin-to-Simpson reading stage," no definition could be further from the truth. Just as history, to the historian, is alive and a part of the continuing pageant of human experience, so is the study of the life of the past a living science to its devotees.

The study of fossils cannot tell us a great deal about the natural forces that shape the evolutionary process, but it does furnish us with guidelines for the consideration of information derived from other sciences. As G. S. Carter[1] has put it, "The part of paleontology in the study of evolutionary theory resembles that of natural selection in the process of evolution; it serves to remove the inefficient but cannot itself initiate." It is clear that we can, and should, present only the most superficial survey of the fossil record and its interpre-

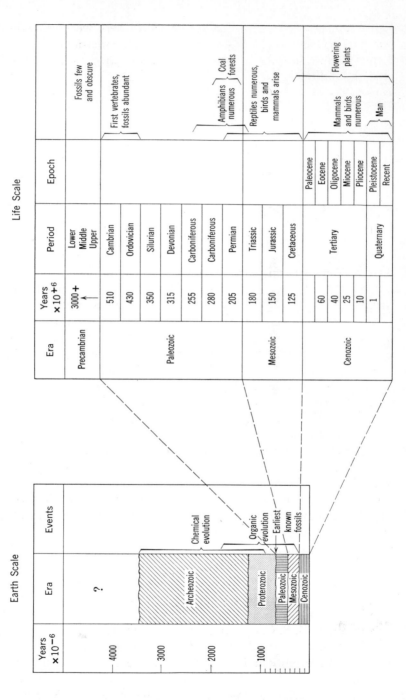

Figure 1. Time scales for the earth and for life on the earth.

THE MOLECULAR BASIS OF EVOLUTION

tation in the present volume. For our purposes here we need only arrive at some general appreciation of the arbitrary divisions of geological time and outline the phylogenetic relationships that exist between the various living and extinct forms of life.

Measurements of the extent of decay of long-lived radioactive elements in the rock strata of the earth's crust enable us to make reasonable estimates of the ages of various strata. Utilizing such data as check points, but relying mostly on time estimates arrived at by classical geological methods, the paleontologist can arrange the fossilized remnants of life in a consecutive order with reasonable accuracy. He can also, in many cases, make certain deductions concerning the relation of specific upheavals and rearrangements of the earth's surface to the changing patterns in the nature and distribution of life as it was in the past.

For the purposes of those interested in the earth sciences, time may be expressed perfectly well on a linear scale, as shown on the left of Figure 1. Such a scale serves to emphasize the relatively small fraction of global time during which life has existed on the earth. The biologist is, however, more naturally preoccupied with "protoplasmic" time and must magnify the portion of the time scale that has to do with living things. The right half of Figure 1 is more useful to the biologist and lists some of the landmarks in evolution, assigned to their proper paleontological time period.

The earliest fossils that occur in any abundance may be assigned to the Cambrian and Ordovician periods and include a large proportion of the basic types of aquatic animals and the possible beginnings of the vertebrates. The record for the Pre-Cambrian period is extremely sparse and is represented mostly by the relatively primitive plants, the algae. At the end of the Pre-Cambrian, most of the invertebrate phyla were relatively well differentiated, although the absence in most instances of structural elements that could survive as fossils makes the reconstruction of their phylogenetic tree somewhat controversial. One scheme is presented in Figure 2. This arrangement of the phyla, which includes the higher vertebrate forms for comparison is, according to its author, L. H. Hyman, not to be taken literally but is only suggestive. It is based on an arrangement of animals in order of structural complexity, without separation of the allied phyla. The bacteria, yeasts, etc., are not shown, for they branched off at some early point in time when the momentous biological accident occurred which led to the establishment of plant and animal kingdoms.

Another way of looking at the phyla is shown in Figure 3, taken

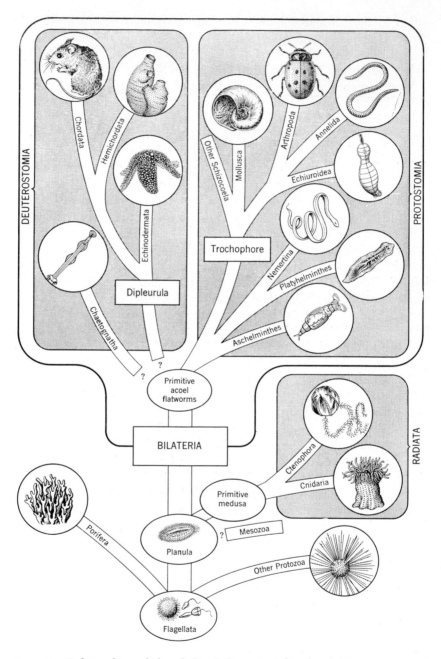

Figure 2. Relationships of the phyla of the animal kingdom. The arrangement here is based on the scheme given by L. H. Hyman in *The Invertebrates*, volume 1, McGraw-Hill Book Company, p. 38, 1940.

from George Gaylord Simpson's fascinating book, *The Meaning of Evolution*. Here we see the major phyla, as they have existed through most of biological time, in terms of their relative abundances. We can observe here some of the correlations between geology and biology which the paleontologist is able to make. For example, the distinct contractions in the abundances of almost all the phyla in the Permian and Triassic periods and the actual extinction of the Graptolithina correlate well with the geological evidence for great mountain building and climatic rigor during these times.

A final illustration for this phylogenetic orientation is given in Figure 4, in which the vertebrates are arranged in their proper ascendency (to use an "anthropophilic" expression). In our discussions of the relations between the biochemistry and genetics of various organisms we shall refer from time to time to the contents of these figures. We shall be interested, for example, in the structure of proteins as they occur in various species and in the possibilities of making some crude estimates from such data of the rates at which specific genes have become modified.

The basic characteristics of the evolutionary process vary considerably, depending on the level of evolution which is being considered. Evolutionary change, measured broadly in terms of the origin of new systems of animal organization, is an expression of *average* change.

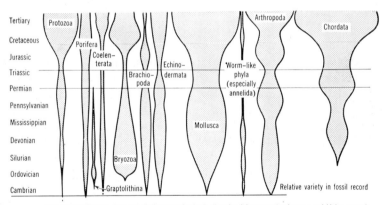

Duration and diversity of the principal groups of animals (based mainly on counts of genera and higher groups)

Figure 3. A schematic diagram of the history of life. The various phyla of animals are represented by paths, the widths of which are proportional to the known variety of each phylum during the various biological periods. Redrawn from G. G. Simpson, *The Meaning of Evolution*, 1950, by permission of Yale University Press.

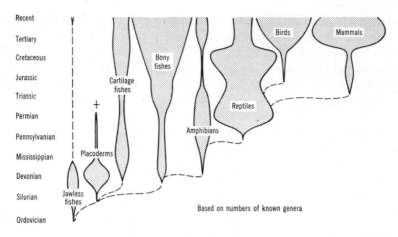

Figure 4. A schematic diagram of the history of the vertebrates. The widths of the pattern for each vertebrate class is proportional to the known varieties of the class in each of the geological periods. Redrawn from G. G. Simpson, *The Meaning of Evolution*, 1950, by permission of Yale University Press.

As Simpson has put it, "It is populations, not individuals, that evolve." As we approach the level of immediate cause and effect, however, certain aspects of evolution become more highly significant, and when we consider a small experimental population of the fruit fly, *Drosophila*, we must become more concerned with individual mutations and their contribution to the survival or death of these specific flies than with theoretical, infinitely large populations. This example is obviously not evolution in the grand sense. It emphasizes "the survival of the fittest," a phrase which, in the light of modern ideas, we know must be replaced with "the survival of the branch of a population which is adapted well enough to its environment to live to procreate." Nevertheless, all evolutionists will agree that the basic cause of change must be gene mutation (although some authors will hold out for the additional involvement of something more ethereal in the way of causation, variously termed "aristogenesis," "*élan vital*," "entelechy," among other names—we shall return briefly to these terms later in this chapter).

As our store of information concerning species variations in biochemical properties, and specifically in protein structure, increases, we will do well to have before us, as a constant frame of reference, a clear picture of the phylogenetic relationships between various forms of life and, particularly, of the time, in terms of numbers of generations, required to accomplish these variations.

THE MOLECULAR BASIS OF EVOLUTION

To develop some appreciation of the magnitude of time involved in the differentiation of a species in relation to that required for a more sweeping phylogenetic change, let us briefly examine those divisions of the process called micro-, macro-, and megaevolution. To quote the capsule summary given by Carter,[1] "There is, first, the origin of the smallest evolutionary differences as seen in continuous series of strata; secondly, there is the differentiation of the members of a group in adaptive radiation; and thirdly, the evolution of a new type of animal organization from its predecessors."

Microevolution

In certain favorable instances, when geological processes have resulted in the formation of a continuous local succession of strata, paleontologists have been able to reconstruct the morphological progression of a species as it took place over many hundreds of thousands of years. An elegant example of such a reconstruction is the work of Trueman[2] and his collaborators on the evolution of the coiled lamellibranch, *Gryphaea*, a mollusk derived from oysters of the genus *Ostrea* which is frequently found in the strata of the Mesozoic era. Mollusks of the genus *Gryphaea* arose frequently and independently from flat-shelled predecessors, presumably in response to the necessity for raising the mouth of the shell above its muddy environment. Four stages in the progressive development of a line of *Gryphaea* are shown in Figure 5. During the evolution from *Ostrea irregularis* to *Gryphaea incurva* a number of morphological characters were modified, and each of these was changed at different rates. Any one of these characters may be used as a measure of *rate* of change; in Figure 6 is shown a plot of the variations in one of these, the number of whorls in the shell, as a function of the vertical location of the sample studied within the superimposed strata. The populations examined by Trueman from any given stratum gave a unimodal distribution curve, strongly suggesting that the population was single and was not a mixture of independent populations.

In a case such as this there is little question that microevolution has occurred without any large and sudden changes (saltations). The general characteristics of the evolution typified by the *Gryphaea*, with its succession of imperceptible gradations and with its uniformity around a mean, led Trueman to suggest that "such an evolving stock must be regarded as a 'plexus' or 'bundle of anastomosing lineages.'" The example has been presented here mainly to illustrate

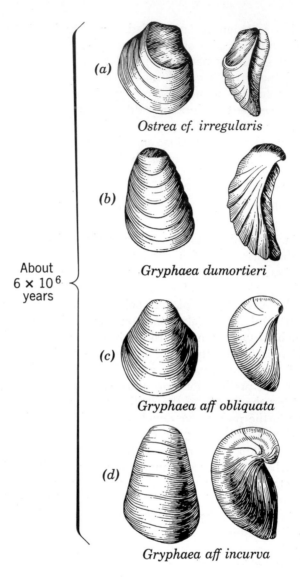

About
6 × 10⁶
years

(a) *Ostrea cf. irregularis*

(b) *Gryphaea dumortieri*

(c) *Gryphaea aff obliquata*

(d) *Gryphaea aff incurva*

Figure 5. Four stages in the evolution of *Gryphaea* from its oyster-like ancestor. Redrawn from A. E. Trueman, *Biol. Revs. Biol. Proc., Cambridge Phil. Soc.,* **5,** 296 (1930).

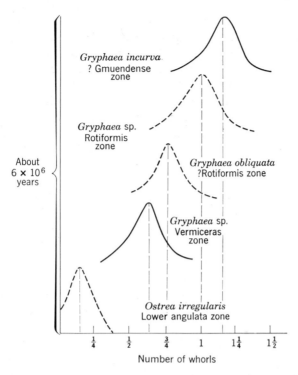

Figure 6. Distribution curves showing the variation in the number of whorls of the shells of successive populations of evolving *Gryphaea*. Redrawn from A. E. Trueman, *Biol. Revs. Biol. Proc. Cambridge Phil. Soc.*, **5**, 296 (1930).

that microevolution is a population phenomenon and that the separate development of radiating lines becomes almost impossible in a restricted population since continual interbreeding prevents the successful rise of deviant groups.

Macro- and Megaevolution

When a mutation confers some benefit on an organism within the framework of the environmental restrictions on the population to which it belongs, the characteristic controlled by the mutant gene may ultimately become firmly entrenched in the heredity of the entire group. However, a limited horizon, such as that available to the *Gryphaea*, permits only a limited phenotypic change. Thus, even though a few "advanced" *Gryphaea* might have appeared which were endowed with some unique and specially favorable character, they would not be likely to be perpetuated as a unique strain because of their random interbreeding with the standard average organism.

The major factor responsible for the larger changes in evolution that lead to distinct new specializations, or to new systems of animal or plant organization, is *adaptive radiation*. Adaptive radiation is the term used by evolutionists to describe the separation of populations into smaller groups having different natural histories. The more mobile the group and the more demanding the environmental changes to which adaptation must be made, the greater the diversity of form (and the number of unsuccessful "experiments"!) that results. This diversity and mobility, together with the concomitant high rate of evolutionary change, make the fossil record scattered and incomplete as opposed to the situation for the sedentary *Gryphaea*. Nevertheless, paleontologists have been able to reconstruct the phylogeny of numerous lines with great success, and certain distinct parameters of macroevolution are well delineated.

The macroevolution of a particular population of organisms leads to great complexity of form, most of the examples of which are false starts and become extinct after a relatively short time (paleontologically speaking). For an evolutionary development to be successful, all the various morphological parts must change in a correlated way to insure survival. The evolutionists can express such correlations in relative growth and development of parts by means of double logarithmic plots, as shown in Figure 7. Here are represented the relations between the heights of the paracones (a cusp of the molar teeth) and the lengths of the ectolophs (the ridge on the outer border of the crown of the same tooth) of the teeth of horses during their progression from the primitive *Eohippus* to the modern animal. Characters that may be related by such straight-line plots (of the general form $Y = bX^k$) are said to be undergoing allometric change, and the slopes of the lines (k) give a measure of the relative rates at which two specific bodily characters are changing.

A sudden modification in the slope of the plot relating two allometric changes indicates a sudden shift in evolutionary direction. For example, such an indication is given several times during the evolution of the horse. As horses underwent adaptive radiation they became exposed to new types of environmental opportunities involving both new kinds of food and new terrain. The changes in the position of the eye and in the structure of the foot and of other physical characteristics have been described in a fascinating way by Simpson in his book *Horses*. The modification of the molars

THE MOLECULAR BASIS OF EVOLUTION

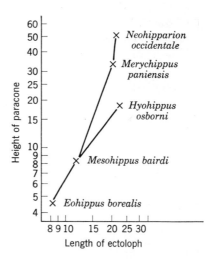

Figure 7. Changes in the structure of the molars during the evolution of the horses. After G. G. Simpson, *Tempo and Mode in Evolution,* 1944, by permission of Columbia University Press.

during equine evolution is particularly instructive in connection with our present consideration of sharp changes in evolutionary direction. As ecological conditions made browsing more favorable than grazing, the whole plan of the molar was modified by natural selection in a direction compatible with the abrasive action of hard grasses. Thus the crown of the molar became thicker and, together with the development of cement, permitted the animals to enjoy a fertile life span in spite of the erosive nature of their natural food supply. A schematic representation of the adaptive radiation of horses is shown in Figure 8. This figure shows the eating habits of the various successive members on the main evolutionary line. The correlative plot of two allometric structural features of the molars, the size of the tooth and its height, shows that there occurred an abrupt increase in the relative height of the tooth in the horses that converted to grazing, whereas in another evolutionary offshoot, *Hyohippus*, which continued to browse on soft, easily chewed plants, such a change did not occur.

Most authorities seem to agree that the evolution of a particular line of organisms, like the horses, can be explained without complication on the basis of the selection of mutants that confer a survival value on the individual and on the population to which he belongs. The occurrence of a particularly advantageous mutation has frequently led to an almost explosive change in structure or habit, and Simpson has proposed the name "quantum evolution" for such major jumps. The view is frequently expressed, however, that the process of natural selection might still be an adequate explanation for these rapid shifts. Their suddenness is perhaps overemphasized because

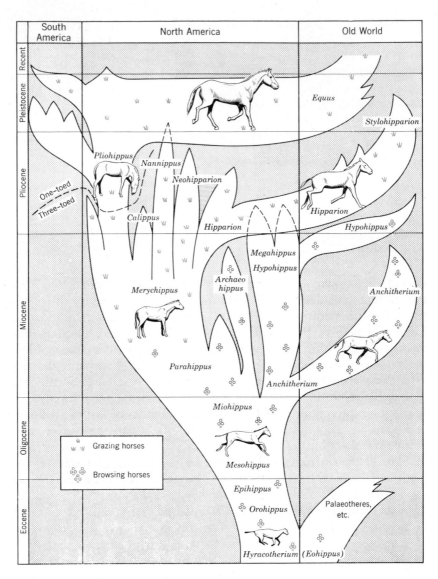

Figure 8. The evolution of the horses. The diagram shows the geographic distribution of the various forms and indicates their manner of securing food by browsing or by grazing. Redrawn from G. G. Simpson, *Horses*, 1951, by permission of Oxford University Press.

THE MOLECULAR BASIS OF EVOLUTION

of gaps in the fossil record that resulted from the rapidity of the changes and the limited geographical region in which they occurred.

In discussions of those portions of evolution in which whole new systems of biological organization arose, the terminology and interpretations of experts becomes varied and, sometimes, delightfully mystical, at least to window-shoppers such as myself. We have already mentioned the terms entelechy, *élan vital,* and aristogenesis. Such terms have been coined to explain (explain *away,* perhaps) the frequent, puzzling phenomena in which new structures and physiologies have arisen in the absence of obvious adaptive value or selective influence. During the evolution of reptiles, for example, there occurred a simplification of the jaw structure which made superfluous the quadrate and articular bones of the reptilian jaw. Ultimately, millions of years later, these "liberated" units became involved in a major change in the structure of the middle ear and made possible the chain of small bones which is characteristic of this organ in mammals. This "aristogenic" change, leading to an entirely new anatomical organization at a much later time, is not easy to explain on the basis of selection and adaptation alone. The phenomenon has implied to some that the evolutionary process has, built into it, some knowledge of the future and that temporarily useless structures may be stored away for later use according to some master plan.

From the standpoint of maintaining a more unified picture of the evolutionary process, "aristogenesis" and the "preadaptation" of an organism for some subsequent evolutionary event do not appear to be necessary concepts. Simpson has pointed out that, in small populations, a mutation which confers no adaptive value (or, indeed, which may be detrimental) *can* become established, although "almost always this would lead to extinction." In those rare cases when the word "almost" applies, a change in the natural history of the organism might then cause an enormously rapid and major evolutionary modification owing to the sudden usefulness of this otherwise disadvantageous gene, fortuitously harbored in the heredity of the strain. From this point of view we may explain the whole of evolution, from the localized, sedentary sort of microevolution to the dramatic appearance of new phyla, on the basis of mutation and selection alone.

As we shall discuss in a later chapter, certain structural parts of biologically active proteins appear to be superfluous from the standpoint of function. A tendency to assume that such parts are nonessential might simply reflect the fact that we have not yet developed sufficiently sensitive methods for the detection of subtle, second-order relationships between structure and function. On the other hand, certain structural configurations may now actually *be* unessential and may have been preserved as chemical vestiges of earlier molecules, much as the bones of the mammalian ear were retained from the re-arranging components of the reptilian jaw.

The information available to us on proteins and other chemical components of protoplasm is, of course, insufficient to permit a rational choice between these alternatives at the present time. We can only hope, in analogy to the paleontologist and his "fossil record," that as the "protein record" relating the proteins of various species to one another becomes more complete, some basic ground plan for phylogenesis and speciation may begin to emerge at a molecular level of understanding.

REFERENCES

1. G. S. Carter, *Animal Evolution; a Study of Recent Views of Its Causes,* Sidgwick & Jackson, Ltd., London, 1951.
2. A. E. Trueman, *Geol. Mag.,* **61**, 360 (1924).

SUGGESTIONS FOR FURTHER READING

Colbert, E. H., *Evolution of the Vertebrates,* John Wiley & Sons, New York, 1955.

Huxley, J. S., *Evolution, the Modern Synthesis,* Allen & Unwin, London, 1942.

Oparin, A. I., *The Origin of Life on the Earth,* translated from the Russian by Ann Synge, Academic Press, New York, third edition, 1957.

Simpson, G. G., *The Meaning of Evolution,* Yale University Press, New Haven, third printing, 1950.

Simpson, G. G., *Horses,* Oxford University Press, New York, 1951.

Simpson, G. G., *Life of the Past,* Yale University Press, New Haven, 1953.

Smith, H. W., *From Fish to Philosopher,* Little, Brown & Company, Boston, 1953.

chapter 2

GENES AS DETERMINANTS
OF HEREDITY

D arwin thought of evolution as a process of adaptation to environment by means of the natural selection of favorable "variations." Within the context of the knowledge of his day he could not, of course, replace the word "variations" with "mutations," since the science of genetics had not yet been invented. However, being a man with a strong urge to tie up loose ends, Darwin suggested that "variations," including those that he felt might be acquired in response to environmental pressures during the lifetime of the organism, were inherited by a mechanism in which all the somatic (body) cells contributed information to the germ cells. We know now that acquired characteristics are *not* inherited and, with the emergence of genetics, it became possible to speak of the inherited characteristics of an organism (his phenotype) as the expression of the sum of his chromosomal genes (his genotype).* We may now

* It should be stressed that environmental conditions, during development, can exert a profound influence on the phenotypic expression of the genes. A classical example of this is the effect of temperature on the number of eye facets in *Drosophila* whose chromosomes bear the mutations "low-bar" and "ultra-bar."[1] Two organisms with identical developmental potentialities may *look* or *act* quite differently, although their respective offspring will be back to the old standard

describe evolution in terms of the natural selection of favorable gene mutations in a population and the perpetuation of these through reproduction.

Since this book is directed at biochemists, many of whom may have had as little formal training in genetics as I have, it is necessary to present, as a starting point for further reading, an abbreviated survey of the gene concept and of some of its experimental consequences. We shall restrict ourselves to the Mendelian genetics of normal bisexual reproduction as it occurs in the higher plants and animals. The mechanisms involved, although by no means universal, can serve as a qualitative basis for considering the reproduction of even such specialized genetic systems as the bacterial viruses, if we are willing to cut some corners.

Nearly a hundred years ago, Gregor Mendel made the observations that established the fundamental laws of genetics. Mendel crossed strains of garden peas which differed in one contrasting character (e.g., purple or white flowers) and observed that the progeny (the so-called F_1 generation) were all purple. This character was, then, the "dominant" trait and white the "recessive." Similar dominance or recessiveness was observed for many other alternative traits.

When two members of the F_1 generation were crossed, he observed that about three-fourths of the progeny in the F_2 generation were purple and one-fourth white. These experiments suggested that any particular character-determining unit of heredity exists in two forms and that these "*allelic*" forms do not blend but maintain their identity throughout the life of the F_1 organisms to separate later in the following generation. The units of heredity were subsequently named "genes" by Johanssen in 1911. An organism, like the F_1 peas of Mendel, which contains both allelic forms is said to be a *heterozygote*, and those possessing a double dose of one or the other allele is a *homozygote*. We refer, genetically, to the former as Rr and to the latter as RR or rr (homozygous for the dominant and recessive forms respectively).

Mendel's experiment, summarized in Figure 9, illustrates the "law of segregation." The frequency of occurrence of purple and white flowered plants in the F_2 generation (3:1) is to be expected if the two allelic forms of this particular color-determining gene, one dominant over the other, segregate to yield equal numbers of R and r units during the formation of germ cells and then proceed to recombine at random in the new generation. Mendel checked this hy-

and the superficial characteristics acquired as the result of environmental pressures will not be inherited.

THE MOLECULAR BASIS OF EVOLUTION

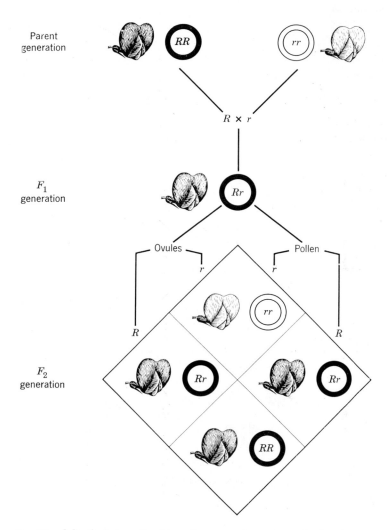

Parent
generation

$R \times r$

F_1
generation

Ovules   Pollen
  r r

R R

F_2
generation

Figure 9. Mendel's first law, the law of segregation; R stands for the gene for purple and r for the gene for white flower color. Black rings and white rings symbolize purple and white-flowered plants, respectively. Purple color is dominant over white. Redrawn from T. Dobzhansky, *Evolution, Genetics, and Man,* John Wiley & Sons, 1955.

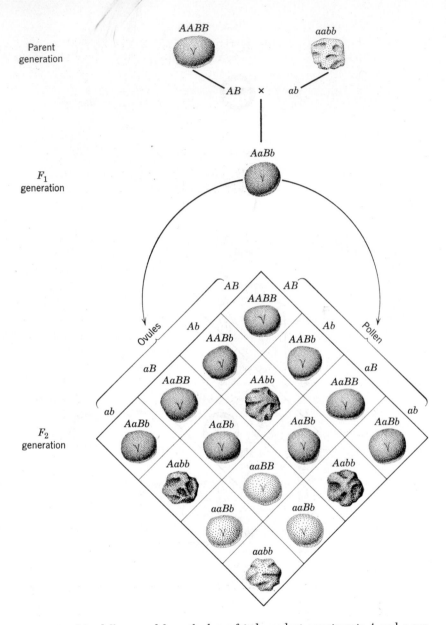

Figure 10. Mendel's second law, the law of independent assortment; *A* and *a* represent the genes for yellow and green colors, respectively, and *B* and *b* those for smooth and wrinkled seed surfaces. Yellow is dominant over green and round is dominant over wrinkled. Redrawn from T. Dobzhansky, *Evolution, Genetics, and Man,* John Wiley & Sons, 1955.

pothesis by allowing the *purple*-flowered plants in the F_2 generation to produce an F_3 generation. One-third of the F_2 plants (the *RR* strain) produced only purple-flowered progeny, whereas two-thirds (the *Rr* variety) produced either white- or purple-flowered progeny in the ratio 1:3 as predicted by the principle of segregation.

In some of his experiments Mendel crossed peas which differed in two or more traits. Thus, as summarized in Figure 10, he crossed peas having yellow, smooth seeds with others having green, wrinkled seeds; he knew in advance that the gene for yellow color was dominant over that for green and the gene for round seeds was dominant over that for wrinkled. The F_1 generation had seeds which were yellow and smooth, since both dominant traits were present in this hybrid and determined the phenotype. In the F_2 generation, however, the phenotype was determined by a random combination of the four segregated traits as shown in the figure. Seeds of the F_2 progeny showed all the four possible combinations of phenotype but, because of the dominance of yellow and smooth over green and wrinkled, these appeared in a ratio of 9:3:3:1 with only one-sixteenth of the seeds having the double recessive characteristics. This phenomenon, *independent assortment* of genetic traits, is the second basic "law" growing out of Mendel's studies.

The simplicity of Mendel's experiments and their ease of interpretation were really due to his good fortune in choosing sets of traits which segregated and recombined to give the theoretical 3:1 ratio. In many instances this ratio is not obtained, and instead certain sets of genes may segregate together to yield what are termed "linked" traits. To understand the linkage of genes we must first consider the phenomena of *mitosis* and *meiosis*.

Cytologists have been aware for over a hundred years of chromosomes as visible rod or thread-like structures that appear in the nucleus during cell division. The number of chromosomes per nucleus is a characteristic constant for any given species. The genetic information present in a cell is accurately perpetuated in each of the daughter cells by the process of *mitosis*. The stages in mitosis are shown in Figure 11 as they are observed in the root tips of the common onion. The simplified drawing on the left side of the figure depicts the behavior of a single chromosome of this plant. The centromeres are represented, in this figure, by open circles. These specialized structures within each chromosomal strand act as points of attachment for the fibers which bind the chromosomes to the pole of the spindle during subdivision of the cell. The centromere is replicated during the division cycle, as shown. Occasional

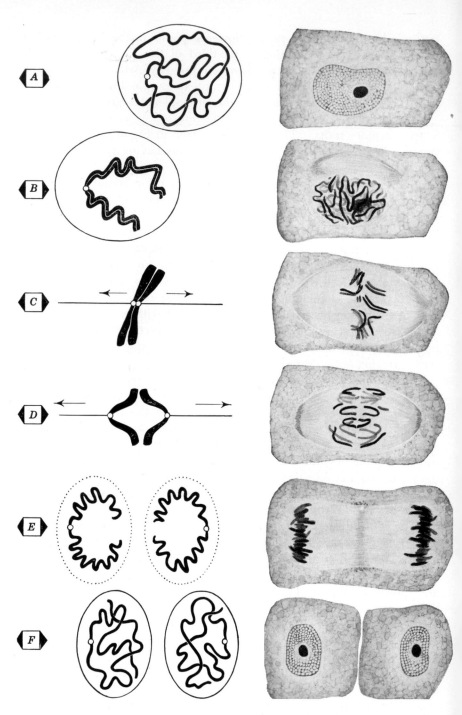

Figure 11. Mitotic cell division in the common onion: *A*, interphase; *B*, prophase; *C*, metaphase; *D*, anaphase; *E*, telophase; *F*, daughter cells. From T. Dobzhansky, *Evolution, Genetics, and Man,* John Wiley & Sons, 1955.

cells containing chromosomes which lack a centromere, or which have more than one, do not survive. The genetically significant event is the exact duplication of each chromosomal daughter-strand during the period between stages *F* and *B*, whereby hereditary constancy is insured in all the somatic cells of an organism during its growth and development.

The nucleus of the somatic cell (diploid) contains twice as many chromosomal strands as the germ cells or *gametes* (haploid). The complement of chromosomal strands in a gamete is the same as that of somatic cells immediately following mitosis, before the machinery of the cell has had an opportunity to bring about duplication of each strand. That is, each gamete contains only a single allelic form of each gene. When two sex cells unite, the resulting diploid *zygote* contains the hereditary units of both parents arranged in such a way that the corresponding chromosomal strands are paired with each set of allelic genes in exact physical complementarity.

When the time comes for the cells of the reproductive tract to produce gametes, there occurs a process termed *meiosis*, which is summarized schematically in Figure 12. The sets of chromosomes first enter a stage resembling prophase in mitosis. The corresponding maternal and paternal chromosome sets then proceed to find one another by a miraculous procedure in which each bit of cytologically discernible detail along the maternal strand pairs with its opposite number in the paternal strand. Each of the two strands then subdivides into two, and, in most organisms, the pairs of strands are bound together at one or more points by "chiasmata" (Figure 12*D*).

The further stages of meiosis lead to the formation of gametes containing only one chromosome of each kind. As shown schematically in the figure, the centromere divides during the second meiotic division. The details of these latter stages of meiosis are somewhat different in different organisms, but the end result, haploid sex cells, is the same.

Early in this century cytologists recognized that the phenomena of independent assortment and segregation of heritable characteristics were consistent with the behavior of chromosomes during cell division. Direct evidence for such a correlation was soon forthcoming, largely through the efforts and imagination of T. H. Morgan. Morgan chose as his experimental object the fruit fly, *Drosophila melanogaster*, which contains extremely large chromosomes in the cells of its salivary glands. This organism possessed a number of important advantages for genetic research, including a high rate of multiplication and a genetic apparatus having only four pairs of chromosomes.

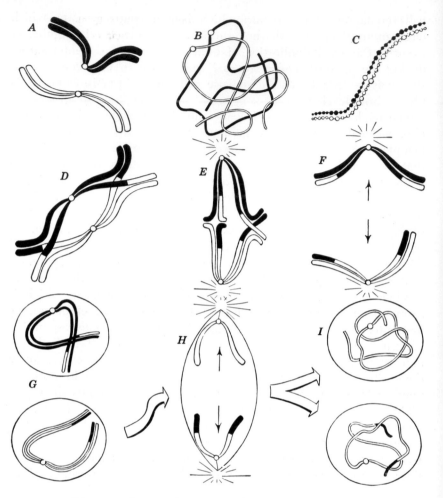

Figure 12. Schematic design of the stages of meiosis. Only a single pair of chromosomes is shown. The paternal chromosomes are in black and the maternal in white. The centromeres are shown as white circles. After T. Dobzhansky, *Evolution, Genetics, and Man*, John Wiley & Sons, 1955.

By crossing strains of flies which showed different inherited traits, Morgan demonstrated that many of these traits behaved according to the principles of Mendelian genetics. He soon observed, however, that a number of traits did *not* show independent assortment but were frequently transmitted from parent to progeny as though they were *linked* together in a genetic bundle. A consideration of the scheme in Figure 12 will make clear the (correct) explanation put forward by Morgan for these observations. Except for the segments of each chromosomal strand that may be exchanged for their counterparts in the course of the formation of chiasmata, the total genetic information in each chromosome appears in any specific gamete as a unit. Thus, two closely linked genes (and we may think of this linkage, in physical terms, as distance along the strand) are not likely to become separated from one another during meiosis. Morgan and his scientific followers in the field soon found that the traits with which they dealt fell into four linkage groups and concluded that each corresponded to one of the four chromosomes. This conclusion was completely supported when subsequent studies on the giant salivary gland chromosomes of *Drosophila* made possible the direct comparison of gene mutations as detected by genetic analysis with visible morphological changes in the individual chromosomes themselves (Figure 13).

Genes that are linked together frequently do show independent assortment, in spite of their location on the same chromosome. This separation is explainable in terms of the exchange of chromosomal segments that takes place between the two strands during the formation of chiasma. (See transfers indicated in Figure 12*D*.) Morgan suggested that the frequency of separation, or of recombination, of two linked genes is a function of the linear distance separating them. Stated in other terms, the probability of a chiasma occurring between two distant genes would be much greater than the probability of one occurring between two genes which are close to one another. His hypothesis has been amply confirmed by a vast amount of data on the recombination of linked genes in a variety of organisms and, although there exist numerous examples of quantitative deviation from the rule, frequency of recombination is in general a reliable measure of the separation between genes.

At this juncture it may be wise to introduce an aside directed toward the novice in genetics. The picture we have drawn of the development of the fundamental concepts of genetics has been made purposely rosy for simplicity's sake. In this discussion, and in what follows, we are interested in getting across only the most basic conceptual framework of the subject and cannot consider the many reservations and qualifications to be found in any adequate textbook. (For example, in male *Drosophila* no chiasmata are formed during the process of spermatogenesis, and consequently no linked genes can undergo recombination in the progenies of hybrid males. In the reproduction of bacteriophage, a matter we shall discuss at greater length in later chapters, recombination of linked genes

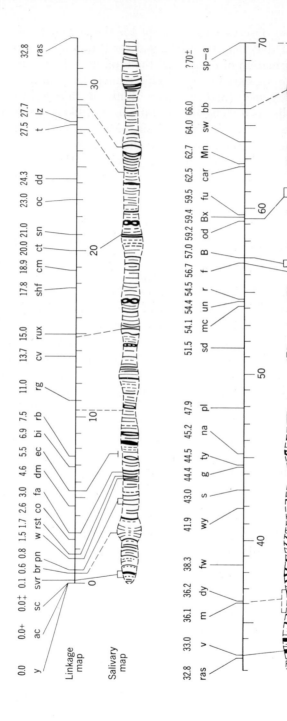

Figure 13. Drawing of the X-chromosome of *Drosophila melanogaster*. The cytological appearance of the salivary gland chromosome can be directly compared with the genetic map constructed from linkage analysis. Redrawn after C. B. Bridges, *J. Heredity*, **26**, 60 (1935).

takes place, *from a statistical point of view*, in a manner quite analogous to recombination in higher organisms. Estimates of the distances between two genes on the phage "chromosome" may be based on the same general sort of calculation that we employ for studies on sweet peas, in spite of the fact that classical reciprocal crossover does not occur; that is, wild-type and double recombinant phages do not, both, generally result from a single mating event.)

If genes may be thought of as being arranged in a linear fashion along the chromosomal strand, and if the distances between them may be estimated by linkage analysis, it is clear that a "map" can be constructed expressing their physical relation to one another. Such maps have been prepared for a number of species of higher organisms and more recently for bacteria and viruses as well. A map of some of the genes that have been studied in *Drosophila melanogaster* is shown in Figure 14. In general, the distances indicated between genes can be shown to be qualitatively correct by internal checks. Thus, in a series of crosses involving three genes A, B, and C, if it is found that the distance between A and B is x units and between B and C is y units, the distance between A and C will be found to be approximately x plus y units. The units used here are "units of recombination" and are merely the percentage of the progeny from any particular cross that is different from either parent genotype. For a variety of reasons, the "genetic distances" indicated on maps such as that shown in Figure 13 bear only a rough correspondence to the actual physical parameters of the chromosomal strand. One factor responsible for such deviations is the apparent greater potentiality of some parts of the chromosome to crossover than others. Another factor involves the occurrence of multiple crossovers. As the length between two genes becomes larger and larger, the chance of multiple crossovers will increase and, in the limit, there will be an equal chance of an even number and an odd number of crossovers. Thus with widely separated genes and with random crossover, the "map distance" would approach 50 recombination units rather than 100. Genetic maps appear, in general, to be a reliable representation of the relative order of genes, confirming the concept of a linear arrangement. But it must be recognized that the frequency of crossover varies from point to point along the chromosome, and from species to species, and has great influence on the additivity of distances and on the total apparent map length.

In the vast majority of cases, the translation of phenotype into the language of genetics follows the simple rules we have attempted to summarize. The difficulties experienced by nonspecialists in the

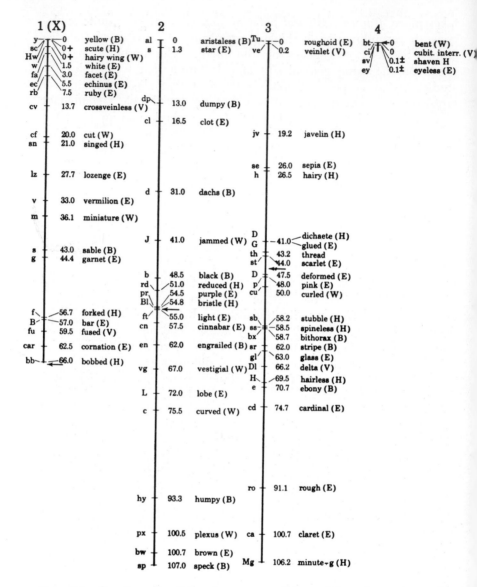

Figure 14. Genetic maps of the chromosomes of *Drosophila melanogaster*. After C. Bridges, from Mary J. Guthrie and John M. Anderson, *General Zoology*, John Wiley & Sons, 1957.

THE MOLECULAR BASIS OF EVOLUTION

course of reading genetic literature arise from the terminology which has been needed by experts to categorize the abnormal. A gene is recognized only because it can be modified and appear in an abnormal allelic form which determines some unusual phenotypic character. We refer to such changes in genes as *mutations,* but we must be constantly aware of the fact that the word has a multiplicity of meanings and that true understanding of genic modification can only be reached when the genetics becomes describable in chemical terms. The appearance of a new phenotypic character may be due to a change in the gene itself, chemical or configurational, to a deletion or reduplication of the gene, or to one of a number of "position effects" involving the inversion or translocation of genes to new positions along the chromosome. As stated by T. Dobzhansky,[2] "A chromosome is not just a container for genes but a harmonious system of interacting genes. The arrangement of genes in a chromosome has developed gradually during the evolution of the organism to which the chromosome belongs; the structure of a chromosome, like the structure of any organ, is a product of adaptive evolution." It is to be hoped that the foregoing discussion of the simplest elements of genetics will be sufficiently irritating in its compactness (and incompleteness) to cause some readers of this book to look into a few of the volumes listed at the end of this chapter.

Most of what follows in this book will be concerned with what genes do, and we approach the subject in terms as chemical as possible within the limits of our present knowledge of nucleic acid and protein structure. In the classical sense, the term "gene" has a purely operational meaning. It may be applied to any unit of heredity that can undergo a mutation and be detected by a change in phenotype. As the determined distances between genes on chromosome maps become less and less, the maximum size of the chemical unit which determines a gene must be thought of as being smaller and smaller. Our impression of the size of a gene, from genetic information alone, depends entirely on the sensitivity of the methods available for the detection of extremely infrequent crossovers. It is precisely within this twilight zone of detectability that the classical definition of the gene begins to break down; here contemporary research in genetics and chemistry finds common ground. Estimates of the size of a gene (as an operational unit) have been made by several methods which together more or less define the upper and lower limits. One sort of estimate is possible from crossover data. Muller and Prokofyeva,[3] for example, localized four genes on the giant salivary gland chromosomes of *Drosophila* within a distance of 0.5 micron and concluded that the upper mean limit of length for each must therefore be 1250 A. Other estimates, derived from studies of the effects of ionizing radiation on the frequency of mutation, indicate that a single gene may occupy a volume corresponding to a sphere with a diameter as small as 10 to 100 A. The discrepancy between crossover and radiation data is considered too large to be due to experimental or interpretative error and suggests that two different aspects of gene structure are being measured by the two techniques, one having to do with the crossover of the entire, intact gene (that is, a functional unit of genetics) and one with the modification of chemical fine structure within its macromolecular architecture.

This conclusion appears to be supported by recent developments in genetic fine-structure analysis, a few of which we shall review subsequently. To establish a bridge between the more classical concepts of genetics and the rather revolutionary findings of the contemporary microbial geneticist, it is instructive to consider an example of the apparent subdivision of a single gene in the genetic material of *Drosophila.*

In the course of linkage analysis, certain genetic units called "pseudoalleles" have been detected which appear to be concerned with the same, or at least with a closely related, function. One such set of pseudoalleles makes up the "lozenge genes" of *Drosophila melanogaster.* A mutation in the "lozenge" region causes changes in the pigmentation of the eyes and also certain other morphological changes. The mutant forms are recessive to the normal allelic form of the gene; that is, heterozygotes show normal pigmentation. Green and Green[4] have studied three mutational loci within this region of the genetic map, all of which have "lozenge" characteristics. From an analysis of crossover data, they have determined that all three loci fall within a genetic distance of less than 0.1 units of recombination. They were further able to show that *double* heterozygotes, in which the *two* mutant alleles were on the same chromosomal strand, showed the wild-type character, whereas an arrangement in which the two mutants appeared on different strands of the same chromosome produced the mutant phenotype. The phenotypic consequences of the various arrangements of two mutant loci are shown in Figure 15. Two explanations for these observations have been offered. One suggests that each of the individual loci controls a different enzymatic activity which is in close physical association with the genetic locus itself. These enzymes are pictured as components of a series of consecutive reactions leading to the formation of an essential chemical material. Such a situation might apply if the individual re-

| Mutant phenotype | (trans) | | | Wild phenotype | (cis) | | |

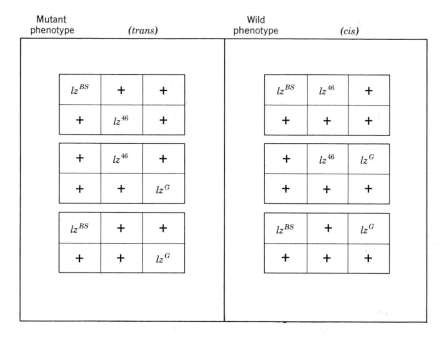

Figure 15. Schematic diagram of the *cis* and *trans* arrangements of the pseudo-allelic "lozenge" genes in *Drosophila melanogaster*. After M. M. Green and K. C. Green, *Proc. Natl. Acad. Sci. U.S.*, **35**, 586 (1949).

actions were of such a nature that the operation of the reaction chain depended on certain minimum concentrations of intermediates and would be interrupted should diffusion (from one chromosomal strand in the "mutant" heterozygotes of Figure 15 to another, for example) lead to a suboptimal concentration level for any of the intermediates. This explanation for pseudoallelism clearly involves a number of rather large assumptions and seems less likely, at the moment, than the second alternative, namely, that each pseudoallelic mutation, although distinguishable, like any "gene," by crossover, is really a change in the *substructure* of the functional parent gene. Thus, we may postulate that a mutation at any of the three loci of the lozenge gene might equally impair its function and that only with the *cis* arrangement, in which one complete unmarred strand carries the load, can the normal phenotype be expressed. To anticipate some of our later discussion, this idea has been used by Benzer as the basis for the coining of a new genetic term, the "cistron," by which is meant a genetic *unit of function* subdivisible by genetic

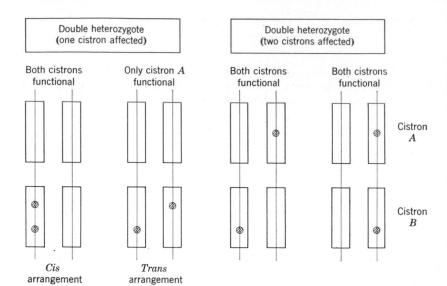

Figure 16. The subdivision of a functional gene into "cistrons," both of which must cooperate to produce an expression in the phenotype. When two mutations occur in the *same* cistron, normal function can only be expressed when the loci are in the *cis* arrangement, but not when they are in the *trans* arrangement. Based on the suggestions of Seymour Benzer, *The Chemical Basis of Heredity*, Johns Hopkins Press, 1957.

tests into ultimate units of recombination termed the "recon." In this system of terminology, two recons would belong to the same cistron when the *cis* arrangement of two mutant loci in a double heterozygote (Figure 16) results in functional adequacy and the *trans* arrangement does not. The demonstration that genes are made up of blocks of very closely linked subunits which may be differentiated by crossover has been a tremendous stimulus to biochemists interested in "genetic chemistry." The mutational effect of ionizing radiation on a bundle of genetic matter having an estimated diameter of 10 A. or so becomes a much more tangible phenomenon when we can compare such a distance with equivalent chemical distances, such as the separation of side chains on a polypeptide or the molecular dimensions of a dinucleotide. As we shall discuss in later chapters, the ultimate mutable units of genetics do, indeed, appear to be about this size, and it is possible that we may soon be able to equate them with individual nucleotide residues along the polynucleotide strands of deoxyribonucleic acid.

An Introduction to the Concept of "Biochemical Genetics"

No summary of genetic principles would be complete without some discussion of heredity in *Neurospora*. *Neurospora* occupies a special niche in genetics because a great deal of the evidence relating genetic constitution to biochemical behavior has been obtained through its study.

It has long been evident that mutations are reflected as changes in biochemical properties. This is essentially a paraphrase of the statement that mutations are detected only because of the difference in phenotype which they induce, the phenotype of an organism presumably being the sum of its biochemical potentialities. The studies on the genetic control of the structure of flower pigments by Lawrence,[5] Scott-Moncrieff, and their colleagues helped establish the fact that individual genes determine the exact chemical structure of these pigments by regulating the extent of methoxylation, hydroxylation, or conjugation with carbohydrate of certain heterocyclic compounds called anthocyans. These studies already began to suggest that the modification of a single gene leads to a change in some specific biosynthetic process.

Wild strains of *Neurospora* may be selected which will grow well on an extremely simple culture medium consisting essentially of sugar, salts, and a single vitamin, biotin. By exposing such cultures to some mutagenic agent (e.g. X-rays), we obtain mutants that no longer grow on the minimal medium but require the addition of nutritional additives like yeast extract and hydrolyzed proteins and nucleic acids. By systematic dissection of the additive mixture, it may be determined which single nutritional requirement has been induced by mutation. The isolation of mutant forms having clear-cut nutritional requirements is not always simple, and many have been isolated which undergo spontaneous reversion to the wild type or which continue to grow on a minimal medium, although at a much reduced rate. However, a large number of stable, full-blown mutants that require a single nutritional additive for growth has now been isolated. These nutritional substances include a variety of amino acids, purines and pyrimidines, and vitamins. Because of the conventional chromosomal system of inheritance, the position of these mutant loci in *Neurospora* may be established by orthodox crossing over methods. The experimental approach to mapping is indicated by a consideration of the natural history of *Neurospora*, the main points of which are shown in Figure 17.

In *asexual* reproduction, the haploid conidia germinate to produce

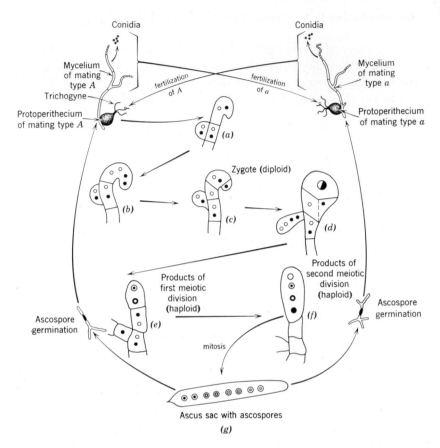

Figure 17. The life cycle of *Neurospora crassa.* The genetic events which occur during the first and second meiotic divisions are illustrated in greater detail in Figure 18. Redrawn, in part, from R. P. Wagner and H. K. Mitchell, *Genetics and Metabolism,* John Wiley & Sons, 1955.

more haploid mycelia. Increase in mass also takes place by simple growth of existing mycelia through mitosis and the utilization of nutrients from the culture medium. In sexual reproduction cross-fertilization takes place between two mating types, variously referred to as A and a, or $+$ and $-$. The conidia of these two types appear to differ only in a single genetic locus on one of the chromosomes. In a cross, the haploid nuclei of the two mating types become associated within a common cytoplasm. In subsequent events (Figure 17) the nuclei of both mating types undergo numerous equational divisions (a,b) and subsequently fuse, side by side, into a diploid pair

THE MOLECULAR BASIS OF EVOLUTION

(c,d). This zygote (d) then undergoes two rounds of meiosis (e,f) to produce four haploid nuclei (f) which then divide mitotically, to yield eight ascospores (g). When these ascospores are exposed to heat or to certain other stimuli (furfural), germination is induced.

One of the advantages of *Neurospora* as an experimental tool in genetics is the fact that the order of events during meiosis is faithfully mirrored in the final asci. As summarized in Figure 17, the upper and lower sets of two nuclei at the four-nucleate stage are derived from the upper and lower nuclei of the binucleate state, and a similar regularity is preserved after the subsequent mitotic division (stage g). The individual ascospores may be dissected out by hand, in order.

With some mutations, which cause a visible difference in the appearance of the final ascospore, we may estimate, without testing the individual spores, the frequency of crossing over during meiosis, and thus the map position of the locus in question in relation to the centromere as a zero point. This procedure is illustrated in an elegant way by an example taken from the work of D. R. Stadler[6] on an unusual lysine-requiring mutant. This mutant, one of a number of lysine-requiring strains studied by N. Good in 1951, exhibits delayed ascospore formation, and mutant spores may be detected within the ascus by their colorless appearance. Perpetuation of this abnormal strain is possible, in spite of the arrested maturation, because the vegetative mycelium can be cultivated indefinitely without the necessity for sexual reproduction and also because an occasional mutant spore will mature upon aging. The photograph in Figure 18 shows the typical appearance of the asci that are produced when the mutant is crossed with a wild-type strain.

The critical stages in meiosis following the cross are shown schematically in Figure 19. The two haploid conidia first fuse to form a zygote a_1. (This zygote is known to be in a double-stranded form (a_2) at the start of the first meiotic division.) During this first meiotic division crossover may or may not occur between the two sets of parental strands. In *Neurospora*, the centromeres from each parental chromosome do not divide during the first meiotic step, and the crossed-over pairs of strands remain attached as shown in the figure (b and c). The frequency of crossing over of a given allele during the first meiosis is assumed to be a function of the distance of this locus from the centromere.

During the second meiotic division each nucleus yields two daughter nuclei to give a total of four, arranged in a row, the upper and lower set derived by division of the upper and lower of the two nuclei in the binucleate cell. If no crossover has occurred, the order shown in *d* develops, whereas *with* crossover four different arrangements may be obtained (*e*). When the four-nucleate cells undergo subsequent mitosis, various asci are produced as shown in the photograph.

The spores containing the mutant locus are easily distinguished by their colorless appearance. Inspection of the photograph (Figure 18) indicates that in nine of the fourteen mature ascospores no crossover has occurred; that is, the normal and the mutant forms of the locus in question have segregated at the first meiotic division.

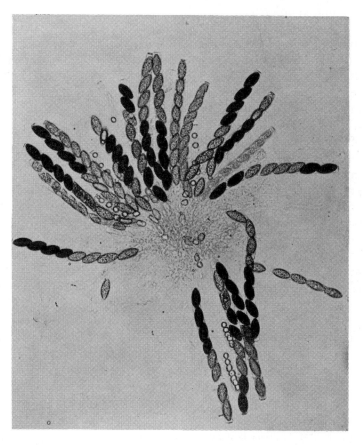

Figure 18. Appearance of asci produced upon crossing a wild-type strain of *Neurospora* with a lysine-requiring mutant which exhibits delayed maturation. As discussed in the text, the approximate location of the mutant locus on its chromosome may be deduced from the relative frequencies of first- and second-division segregation. This photograph was obtained through the kindness of Dr. David R. Stadler of the University of Washington.

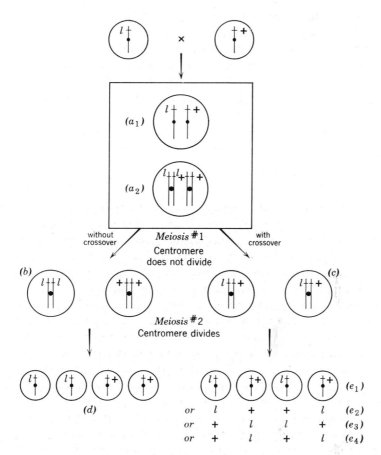

Figure 19. A schematic diagram of the genetic events which occur during the development of an ascus from a zygote in *Neurospora*. The left side of the diagram shows the results of first division segregation, and the right side, those of second division segregation of the two alleles, *l* and +.

Five ascospores show a pattern consistent with *second* division segregation, one alternating as in Figure 19, e_1 and e_4, and four symmetrical as in e_2 and e_3. Therefore, five-fourteenths of the mature ascospores, during development from zygotes, have undergone crossover. Assuming linearity of genes, a direct relationship between crossover frequency and linear distance, and the absence of centromere division in the first meiosis, the mutant locus would be calculated to be $\frac{5}{14} \times 100$ or 36 per cent of the distance from the centromere to the end of the chromosomal strand. (Actually this map distance is to be divided by a factor of two since the unit of mapping in *Neurospora* is defined as one-half of this ratio.)

The crossover frequency values obtained from cross to cross were found by Stadler to vary over a considerable range, as is frequently observed in genetic practice. *Accurate* mapping must always involve a series of crosses between three separate markers or two markers and the centromere, so that additivity may be used as a check. This example is included here because it illustrates how an approximate estimate may be made of the location of a mutant locus in *Neurospora*, even without exhaustive crossing of progeny, when the mutation produces a visible change in the convenient ascospore "recording system."

The great value of the *Neurospora* mutant technique as a tool for relating genetics to biochemistry will be evident from a consideration of the following example. Three genetically distinct mutants, which will grow on the minimal medium when this is supplemented with one or more of the three amino acids, arginine, citrulline, and ornithine, have been isolated. Mutant 1 can grow only when supplied arginine and cannot utilize citrulline or ornithine. Mutant 2 can use both citrulline and arginine, and mutant 3 can manage on any one of the three nutritional additives. These observations suggest that arginine may be produced through the sequence of reactions shown in Figure 20. Assuming the correctness of this biochemical hypothesis, we may propose that the mutant loci in the three mutants each affect a specific enzymatic process in the reaction chain leading to the synthesis of arginine. The correctness of this proposition is indicated by the fact that nutritional mutants will, in general, utilize and grow on intermediates that come after the "block" but not those that precede it. Indeed, in most instances, there is an accumulation of intermediate metabolites preceding the block.

The particular reaction sequence leading to arginine formation is a well-established one for many organisms. The study of the three *Neurospora* mutants is, thus, mainly a confirmatory one, but it has great historical interest since it was one of the earlier clean-cut examples of the direct relation between the enzymatic potential of an organism and its heredity. In many later investigations results derived from the study of other mutants have frequently served as the first wedge in the elucidation of new metabolic pathways.

Perhaps the most significant development growing out of the study of the inheritance of nutritional requirements in *Neurospora* has been the enunciation of the "one gene–one enzyme" hypothesis by G. W. Beadle and E. L. Tatum and their collaborators. This hypothesis, which proposes that a single gene controls the synthesis of only one enzyme or other specific cellular protein, can be made quite flexible by the proper choice of semantics. The breadth of interpretation is

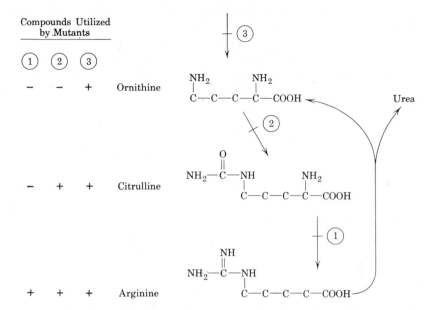

Figure 20. A series of biochemical reactions in the biosynthesis of arginine, the order of which could be established by the study of the nutritional requirements of three mutants of *Neurospora*. From the work of A. M. Srb. and N. H. Horowitz, *J. Biol. Chem.*, **154**, 129 (1944).

directly dependent on the definition we choose to give to the word "gene." Thus, as is true of the pseudoalleles of the "lozenge" gene in *Drosophila*, finer and finer genetic analysis begins to discriminate between loci which are part of the same functional unit. In a relatively coarse analysis, such as the study of the three mutants in the arginine pathway, we are not able to say with certainty whether the blocked step in mutant 2, for example, is immediately prior to citrulline or whether one of a number of intermediate steps between ornithine and citrulline is blocked instead. At the other extreme, an exhaustive genetic analysis might permit the detection of two genetic loci separated by so small a distance along the genetic strand that they would be part of the same functional unit. Mutation of either of these might alter or abolish the biological activity of the same protein molecule. This situation has, indeed, been observed for a number of microorganisms and bacteriophages, and much of what follows in this book will deal with this theme.

One excellent example of a direct relationship between a single protein and a single gene is the case of the two types of tyrosinase in *Neurospora*. Horowitz[7] and his colleagues have shown that the mutation of a single genetic locus causes the formation of a heat-labile tyrosinase which is indistinguishable from the usual, heat-stable enzyme in all other physical and kinetic properties. The two forms of the enzyme may be isolated in quite pure form, and there can be no doubt that the genetic modification affects a single protein molecule. The difference between the two forms of the enzyme is inherited in a strictly Mendelian way; that is, a given pure strain of *Neurospora* produces only one form of the enzyme, and the progeny of a cross between the two strains are identical with one or the other parent strain in equal proportion.

The possibilities suggested by this and other similar gene-protein relationships are among the most intriguing in the whole of biology. Clearly, if slight modifications in protein structure can ultimately be equated with equally slight changes in the molecular structure of genetic material, there will be opened to us a whole new area of research and speculation on the most basic aspects of the evolutionary process.

REFERENCES

1. J. Krafka, *J. Gen. Physiol.*, **2**, 409 (1920).
2. T. Dobzhansky, *Evolution, Genetics, and Man*, John Wiley & Sons, New York, 1955.
3. H. J. Muller and H. A. Prokofyeva, *Compt. rend. acad. sci.*, U.R.S.S., **4**, 74 (1934).
4. M. M. Green and K. C. Green, *Proc. Natl. Acad. Sci. U.S.*, **35**, 586 (1949).
5. W. J. C. Lawrence, in *Biochemical Soc. Symposia, Cambridge, Engl.*, No. 4 (1950).
6. D. R. Stadler, *Genetics*, **41**, No. 4, 528 (1956).
7. N. H. Horowitz and M. Fling, in *Enzymes: Units of Biological Structure and Function*, (O. G. Gaebler, editor), Academic Press, New York, p. 139, 1956.

SUGGESTIONS FOR FURTHER READING

Catcheside, D. G., *The Genetics of Micro-Organisms*, 1951, Pitman Publishing Corporation, New York.
The Chemical Basis of Heredity (W. D. McElroy and B. Glass, editors), Johns Hopkins Press, Baltimore, 1957.
Pontecorvo, G., in *Advances in Enzymology*, volume 13, Interscience Publishers, New York, p. 121, 1952.
Wagner, R. P., and H. K. Mitchell, *Genetics and Metabolism*, 1955, John Wiley & Sons, New York.

chapter 3

THE CHEMICAL NATURE

OF

GENETIC MATERIAL

There can be little doubt that the major share of the heredity of a strain is carried in the chromosomes of its germ cells. This conclusion is based firmly on the observations of the cytologist and the geneticist that specific mutations may be directly related to localized morphological changes in chromosomes. It serves as the starting point for one of the most thriving enterprises in modern biological research, namely, the identification and chemical description of genetic material. Progress has been rapid and we can now state with some assurance that the substance most directly associated with the storage and perpetuation of hereditary information is the deoxyribonucleic acid (DNA) of the chromosomal strands.

Aside from the circumstantial evidence furnished by the cyto-chemical localization of DNA in chromosomes, there are a number of other lines of evidence which give more explicit information bearing on this idea. It was demonstrated by Boivin, Vendrely, and Vendrely[1] in 1948, for example, that the DNA content of somatic cells (diploid) was constant from tissue to tissue in a single species but that sperm cells (haploid) contained exactly half as much.

These observations were extended to a number of other species by Mirsky[2] and his collaborators. The latter group also showed that the distribution and quantities of various other chemical components of nuclei generally *did not* correlate in a way to be expected for genetically critical material. We know that the nucleus contains, in addition to DNA, ribonucleoprotein, various arginine-rich protamines and histones, a tryptophan-rich protein fraction, and a small amount of lipid. None of these substances (with the exception of the protamine-histone fraction, which may be directly associated with DNA) appears to have the constancy of distribution from cell type to cell type within a species of the sort exhibited by the DNA component.

Another type of experimental observation which suggests a genetic role for DNA is concerned with the effects of mutagenic agents, such as ultraviolet radiation and certain chemicals. It has been shown that the efficiency spectrum of ultraviolet light in producing mutations is closely related to the absorption spectrum of nucleic acid. Such experiments are not completely convincing in themselves since the absorption of ultraviolet photons by the nucleic acid molecule might conceivably be only the first step in a chain of reactions in which the final target could reside in molecules of a rather different chemical nature. Experiments on the mutagenic effect of such agents as mustard gas are similarly inconclusive since, although the nucleic acids do appear to be much more chemically reactive to these substances *in vitro* than are the proteins, we cannot discount the special sensitivity of a particularly important member of the latter class of compounds. In spite of these possible objections, there is a certain amount of direct evidence which indicates that when we tamper with the chemical structure of DNA, be it by radiation or by chemical techniques, the rate of mutation is increased. Zamenhof[3] and his colleagues have shown that when the thymine analogue, 5-bromouracil, is incorporated by a cell into the structure of its DNA, the frequency of mutation is greatly increased. The reasons for this stimulation of the mutation rate may be related to the presence of the abnormal pyrimidine base in the polynucleotide sequence of the DNA molecule, or it may equally well be the result of some aberration in the kinetics of the biosynthesis of DNA. Whatever the reason, we may at least conclude that the DNA molecule is implicated in this chemically induced mutagenesis.

The metabolic stability of DNA also supports the close association of DNA with genes. In spite of a number of early misleading reports, the consensus now clearly indicates that the DNA content of chromosomes does not change during the stages of division, nor do the subcomponents of its structure undergo equilibration with extra-nuclear sources of DNA precursors. The most clear-cut support for this conclusion comes from cytochemical and radiochemical studies on the nuclei and chromosomes of growing tissues, particularly of plants. Howard and Pelc,[4] for example, attacked the problem by growing roots of the English broad bean, *Vicia faba*, in the presence of radioactive orthophosphate. Autoradiographs of squash preparations of the root tissue were then prepared by the stripping film technique. An analysis of the way in which radioactivity was associated with the nuclei in various stages of division and in the resting stage indicated that incorporation of the isotope takes place only in the resting, interphase nucleus and that prophase and metaphase nuclei are not actively synthesizing nucleic acid. Autoradiographs of root tips which had been incubated with isotope for more extended periods permitted the further conclusion that the tagged nucleic acids of the chromosomes are passed on to daughter cells without intermediate degradation and resynthesis. These experiments, and the resulting conclusions, have been greatly refined, both as the result of improvements in the technique of chromosome autoradiography and by the study of purified isotopically labeled DNA from various sources. We shall return to these more recent studies after we have first considered the chemistry of DNA and the organization of the chromosome in more detail. However, the experiments of Howard and Pelc, even without embellishment, are quite satisfying from the genetic point of view since they suggest conservation of DNA and the physical continuity of the gene during cell replication.

Some of the best evidence for the central importance of DNA in genetics comes from studies on "transformation." This phenomenon, discovered in pneumococcus by F. Griffith in 1928, has since been extended to a number of other microorganisms. It involves the change in the genotype of one strain of cells that is produced by exposure to extracts of cells of a different strain.

Pneumococci generally exist in two forms. One forms "smooth" colonies on agar plates, possesses a type-specific polysaccharide capsular substance, and is virulent. The other forms "rough" colonies and lacks both the virulence and the polysaccharide of the smooth form. The smooth forms are genetically stable, and a strain characterized by a Type II polysaccharide, for example, does not spontaneously mutate to Type III. "Smooth" organisms do, however, mutate to rough forms, and this conversion appears to be irreversible. Griffith showed that when mice were subjected to mixed injections of living non-encapsulated "rough" organisms and killed "smooth" organisms, living encapsulated bacteria could be isolated from the animal. The *progeny* of these transformed bacteria were also encapsulated, and the specific polysaccharide was shown to persist indefinitely through successive generations until spontaneous mutation to a rough form occurred.

Avery and his collaborators,[5] and later Hotchkiss, Zamenhof, and others, have shown that the substance in Griffith's extracts which is responsible for the transformation has the chemical characteristics of DNA.[6] The evidence for this is now very convincing, and the transformation of organisms for a host of genetic markers in addition to that controlling encapsulation can now be attributed, with relative certainty, to the DNA molecule. The transformation is definitely not caused by a protein contaminant.

Many of the DNA-borne characters were originally selected by exposure of bacteria to sink-or-swim situations (Figure 21). For example, when pneumococci are grown in the presence of streptomycin, essentially all the cells are killed by the drug. A very few cells, however, survive and continue to multiply, producing a culture which is resistant to the levels of streptomycin employed. These organisms have acquired, by a chance mutation, the physiological characteristics which permit them to occupy a new "ecological niche" in nature (although a rather unnatural one). Not only do the cells which survive streptomycin behave as a new and constant phenotype, but samples of DNA prepared from them possess the ability to transform other cells to a state of streptomycin resistance.

The genetic stability of transformable traits is highly suggestive of true gene transfer. It is difficult, however, to prove unequivocally that actual chromosomal material is being transferred by this process from cell to cell. The chemistry and cytology of bacterial nuclei is still quite obscure and, to make matters more difficult, genetic analysis of the sort that can be done with sweet peas or *Drosophila* is not easy with bacteria because multiplication takes place most commonly by mother-daughter division rather than by sexual mating. Sexual mating does take place fairly frequently in some microorganisms, and it seems likely that the transmission of transformed characters as unit particles of heredity could be studied by some direct hybridization technique if the proper choice of bacterium and other transformable traits were combined in one experimental system. To my knowledge, however, such a study has not been carried out for any of the traits that can be transferred by a purified DNA preparation.

THE MOLECULAR BASIS OF EVOLUTION

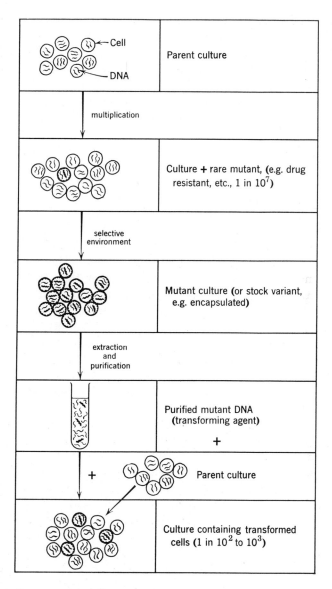

Figure 21. Experimental steps in the transformation of a bacterial culture. Redrawn from R. Hotchkiss, *The Nucleic Acids,* volume 2 (E. Chargaff and J. N. Davidson, editors), Academic Press, 1954.

There are, however, in addition to genetic stability, several other features of transformation that support the notion that the transfer of unit characters by DNA is closely analogous to the normal genetic process occurring during cell division. It has been shown, for example, that the DNA prepared from strains of bacterial cells which have been transformed for two transformable markers can occasionally produce simultaneous transformation for both traits, as though these were linked on the same "chromosomal" fragment. Thus, Marmur and Hotchkiss[7] have selected, from a strain of streptomycin-resistant pneumococci, mutants that have also undergone a mutation which permits them to ferment mannitol. When DNA preparations from such doubly labeled cells were added to a culture of "wild-type" pneumococci, three distinct types of transformed bacteria could be isolated. The majority were either transformed for streptomycin resistance *or* for mannitol utilization, but some individual cells had clearly been transformed for both characters. The frequency of double transformation was considerably greater than the product of the frequencies of the two single transformations, an observation which is genetically interpretable only in terms of the linked transfer of two unit characters by a single event. This observation, so reminiscent of linkage in the chromosomes of higher organisms, certainly suggests that a single fragment of DNA can contain the information for the elaboration of two distinct physiological systems and that this fragment represents a piece of the normal genetic material of the bacterial cell from which it was derived.

These studies have since been extended by Hotchkiss and his colleagues to cells that contain three transformable markers. They have shown that, during transformation with DNA, these markers may remain linked, be separated, or be reassembled by recombination in a manner completely analogous to that observed with doubly marked cells. In spite of our ignorance of the details of the process, we may conclude with reasonable certainty that the mechanical transfer of genetic information from cell to cell by purified DNA represents a good model for some of the events that occur during conventional gene transfer in dividing cells.

Chemical Structure of DNA

One of the most fascinating recent developments in biochemistry has been the study of the structure of deoxyribonucleic acid, both from the standpoint of its molecular composition and in terms of the arrangements of its component parts in three dimensions. If DNA is to be established as the substance responsible for the transmission of heredity at the molecular level, we should be able to demonstrate that the morphological behavior of chromosomes can be explained as a function of the structure and metabolism of DNA. Amazingly enough, such a picture has begun to emerge as the result of a series of very skillful experiments and deductions. There are the usual inconsistencies and hopeful extrapolations, but the present outlook is certainly an optimistic one.

In 1948 the conception of DNA as a regular array of repeating tetranucleotide units was seriously shaken by the fundamental studies[8] of Vischer and Chargaff and of Hotchkiss, who showed by chromatographic techniques that the four heterocyclic bases in DNA are not present in equal amounts and that there are actually more than four such bases in some samples of DNA. Since these studies, the list of naturally occurring purines and pyrimidines in the DNA molecule has grown to seven, and a complete reappraisal of the structural details of DNA has taken place.

By an examination of the products produced from DNA by acid or enzymatic hydrolysis we may deduce that the successive stages of degradation are as follows: *

DNA → nucleotides → nucleosides + phosphoric acid →
                      purine and pyrimidine bases + deoxyribose

The chemical structure of these substances is indicated in Figure 22. In most samples of DNA, four heterocyclic bases predominate—the purines adenine and guanine and the pyrimidines thymine and cytosine. However, some samples of DNA (e.g. from wheat germ and the grasses in general) contain 5-methylcytosine in large amounts and, indeed, this derivative of cytosine is found in small quantity in preparations from mammalian tissue as well. The DNA prepared from the "even" members of the T bacteriophages (T2, T4, and T6) contains 5-hydroxymethylcytosine instead of cytosine. An unusual purine, 6-methylaminopurine has been found in the DNA of certain bacteria. For general purposes of discussion, however, we shall take as prototypes only the four common bases.

* The hydrolysis of *ribo*nucleic acid (RNA), approximately nine-tenths of which is found in the cytoplasm of cells and one-tenth in the nucleus, yields the same set of products except for *ribose* in place of *deoxyribose,* and *uracil* in place of *thymine* (see Figure 22). The bonds that join the nucleotide residues in RNA are basically similar to those in DNA, but much less is known about its molecular configuration. The presumed role of RNA in the biosynthesis of proteins is discussed in Chapter 10.

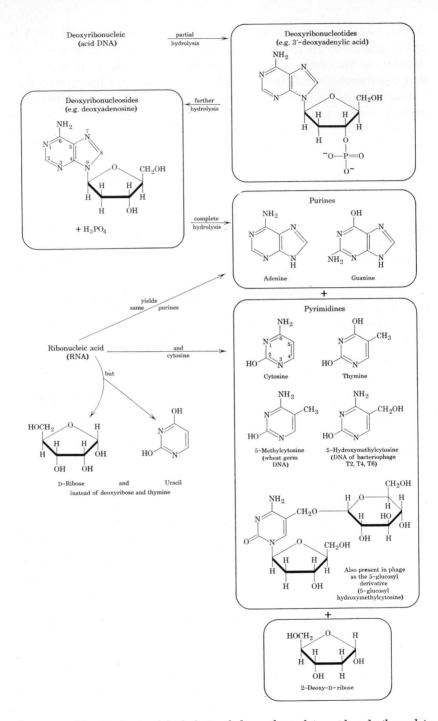

Figure 22. The products of hydrolysis of deoxyribonucleic acid and ribonucleic acid.

The sugar, deoxyribose, together with the phosphate residues, forms the chemical backbone of the DNA molecule. Since deoxyribose has only three hydroxyl groups, and since one of these, at carbon 1, is bound in an N-ribosidic linkage to one of the four heterocyclic bases, the alternating phosphate residues must be doubly esterified with the hydroxyl groups on positions 3 and 5. On the basis of this information, we may already depict the general structure of DNA as shown in Figure 23. To round out the purely chemical part of the DNA structure we need only assign to the various 1 positions of the deoxyribose units the proper choice of purine or pyrimidine base.

This is a very large order. The composition of DNA varies a great deal from source to source and, even more serious, there is now good evidence that most samples of DNA are probably heterogeneous and may represent a mixture of molecules with differing base contents and sequences. In spite of these difficulties, the analytical study of many DNA samples from a host of biological sources has established the following relationships, which hold more or less quantitatively throughout Nature.

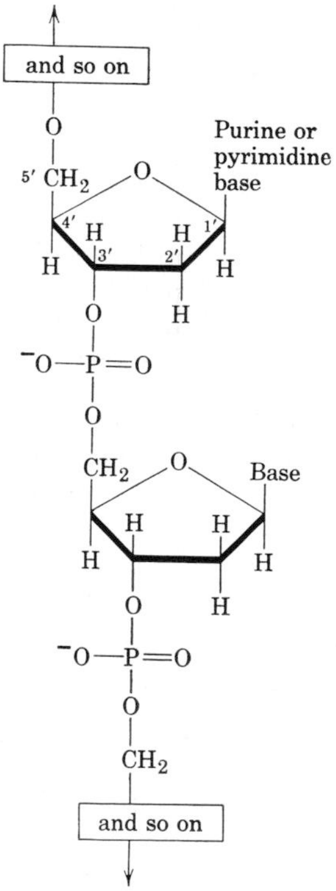

Figure 23. The nature of the linkage between individual deoxyribonucleotides in deoxyribonucleic acid. Individual nucleotide residues in the DNA chain are linked through 3′-5′ phosphate diester bridges. The carbon atoms of the deoxyribose moiety are numbered 1′, 2′, etc. The carbon and nitrogen atoms of the purine and pyrimidine rings are numbered 1, 2, 3, etc., without the primes (see Figure 22).

1. There is a stoichiometric equality between the sum of the purines and the sum of the pyrimidines.

2. There is equivalence in the contents of adenine and thymine, and of guanine and cytosine (or the sum of cytosine and its less common derivatives when these are present). Two types of DNA may be recognized, the first in which the sum of adenine plus thymine is larger than the sum of guanine and cytosine (the AT type), and the reverse (the GC type) which occurs mainly in the micro-organisms.

3. The content of 6-amino groups equals the content of 6-keto groups.

We have, then, a set of requirements which data on the sequence of bases, now meager but rapidly accumulating, must fit. These

TABLE 1

The distributions of Deoxycytidylic Acid (C) and 5-Methyldeoxycytidylic Acid (M) among the Dinucleotides from Calf Thymus DNA Produced by Digestion with Pancreatic Deoxyribonuclease[9]

C-Dinu-cleotide	Mole Fraction of Digest	M-Dinu-cleotide	Mole Fraction of Digest
C–p–C–p–	1.11	M–p–M–p–	0
C–p–T–p–	0.78	M–p–T–p–	0
T–p–C–p–	2.34	T–p–M–p–	0
C–p–A–p–	0	M–p–A–p–	0
A–p–C–p–	3.22	A–p–M–p–	0
C–p–G–p–	0.75	M–p–G–p–	0
G–p–C–p–	0.12	G–p–M–p–	1.03

The abbreviated formulas for dinucleotides (T–p–C–p– for example) repre-sent the phosphate diesters formed by two mononucleotides, joined in the manner illustrated in Figure 23.

restrictions, in themselves, tell us that DNA molecules must be con-structed according to a meaningful plan and that the arrangement of heterocyclic bases must be of great importance in the functional properties of DNA. Other available evidence strongly suggests that the sequence of bases is anything but random. For example, Sins-heimer[9] has isolated from partial hydrolysates of DNA a large series of dinucleotide fragments, some of which are shown on the left side of Table 1. Some of the sequences listed are much more common than others. Recently, Shapiro and Chargaff[10] have reported on their similar fractionation studies and concluded that at least 70 per cent of the pyrimidines in various DNA samples occur as oligonucleotide "tracts" containing three or more pyrimidines in a row and that this sort of lumping, because of the three equality relationships listed, must, therefore, also be true of the purines.

This is about as far as we can go at the moment with the critical problem of the sequence of bases. There has been, however, a dramatic advance in connection with the three-dimensional aspects of DNA structure. A large part of this advance stems from the elegant X-ray diffraction studies of M. H. F. Wilkins and his colleagues on DNA from several sources. The X-ray patterns they obtained were all remarkably similar and suggested that there existed some uniform molecular pattern for all deoxyribonucleic acids. Their data were consistent with the presence in DNA of two or more polynucleotide chains arranged in a helical structure and permitted the calculation of the rough dimensions of the helix.

Employing the data of Wilkins and his collaborators,[11] and taking into consideration the various restrictions on base pairing and stoichiometry, J. D. Watson and F. H. Crick[12] were able to construct a model which accommodates most of the experimental facts. This model, in spite of slight stereochemical shortcomings which have since been adjusted by Wilkins and his colleagues (Figure 24), has been a tremendously valuable stimulus to the field of nucleic acid chemistry as well as to genetics. The Watson-Crick model was based, in addition to the analytical data on base content and the X-ray results, on the fact that titration studies had indicated that the polynucleotide chains in the DNA molecule were joined together through hydrogen bonding between the base residues. The critical assumptions made by Watson and Crick were that the number of chains in the molecule was two, and that there was a specific sort of base pairing which made each pair symmetrical and equivalent in relation to the cross-linking of the two sugar-phosphate backbones. The base pairs required by the model, adenine-thymine and guanine-cytosine, are shown in Figure 25, joined together through hydrogen bonds. The formulas shown in the figure are drawn from the work of Linus Pauling and Robert Corey,[13] who have considered the DNA double-helix model in detail in relation to the crystal structure data for purines and pyrimidines. Their results, which show that three hydrogen bonds can be formed between cytosine and guanine, indicate that an even greater specificity of base pairing is inherent in the DNA model than was suggested by the considerations of Watson

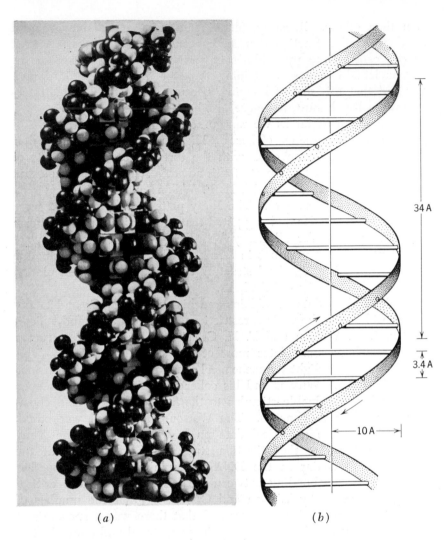

(a) (b)

Figure 24. Photograph of a molecular model of deoxyribonucleic acid (through the courtesy of Dr. M. H. F. Wilkins). A schematic drawing of this two-stranded structure is shown on the right, together with certain of its dimensions.

and Crick, who assumed that two hydrogen bonds are formed between each base pair.

The model has the interesting feature that the two strands of polynucleotide are complementary to one another and that the arrangement of bases on one strand fixes the arrangement on the

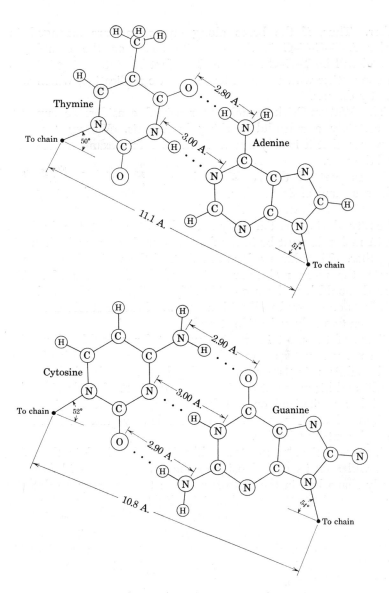

Figure 25. The pairing of adenine and thymine (top) and cytosine and guanine (bottom) by means of hydrogen bonding. Redrawn after L. Pauling and R. B. Corey, *Arch. Biochem. Biophys.*, **65**, 164 (1956).

other. Thus, if the bases along one strand are arranged in the order A–G–G–T–C–A, the opposite bases on the complementary strand will be T–C–C–A–G–T. This fact has interesting implications in connection with the process of genetic replication, which we shall shortly discuss.

The Watson-Crick model has received considerable support and is certainly a splendid working hypothesis. We must remember, however, that it is only a model and therefore examine both the pros and the cons.

In support of the double helix can be offered the studies of Thomas[14] and of Schumaker, Richards, and Schachman.[15] Both have concluded, from investigations of the changes in light scattering and viscosity during partial enzymatic digestion, that the bulk of the DNA molecule must be in the form of double chains which are linked together. They have calculated that, if the molecule were a single chain, the mean molecular weight of the fragments of DNA produced should have been considerably smaller than observed and that the facts correspond well with a system of rather stable cross-linkages between two polynucleotide strands.

Some of the most impressive support for a double-stranded, complementary structure comes from the very recent work of Meselson and Stahl[16] using an ultracentrifugal method developed by Vinograd[17] and his group at the California Institute of Technology. Vinograd has capitalized on the fact that strong salt solutions (e.g. of cesium chloride) may be forced into a density gradient when exposed to high centrifugal fields.

A macromolecular substance like DNA dissolved in the salt solution will seek its own density in the gradient and will form a relatively sharp line in the centrifugal cell; the line may be detected by its strong absorption of ultraviolet light. If two species of DNA that differ in density are present, these will separate and form two distinguishable zones (Figure 26). In this way it is possible to estimate, for example, the relative proportions of normal DNA and of DNA containing the rather dense pyrimidine, bromouracil, in a mixture of the two.

Meselson and Stahl grew *Escherichia coli* in a nutrient medium containing nitrogen of mass 15 exclusively and thus obtained a population of organisms which were fully labeled with this isotope. They then transferred cells, taken during the logarithmic phase of growth, to a medium containing N^{14} precursors. Samples were taken when the population had doubled and again after a second doubling. Deoxyribonucleic acid was prepared from the original fully labeled

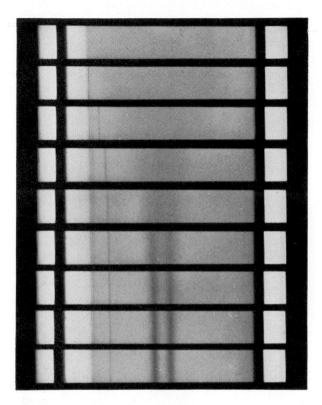

Figure 26. The density gradient centrifugation of a mixture of N^{15}- and N^{14}-labeled deoxyribonucleic acids from *E. coli*. Exposures were taken every 128 minutes. Equilibrium has been attained by the time of the eighth or ninth photograph. The molecular weight of the DNA is approximately 10,000,000. From M. Meselson and F. W. Stahl, *Proc. Natl. Acad. Sci. U.S.*, **44**, 671 (1958).

cells and from the two batches of cells that had undergone multiplication. Each of these preparations was then dissolved in strong cesium chloride solution, having a density in the neighborhood of the apparent density of DNA, and centrifuged until density equilibrium had been attained in the ultracentrifuge cell. Reproductions of the distribution patterns obtained are shown in Figure 27. The DNA prepared from the fully labeled bacteria gives a single band corresponding to the density to be expected for N^{15} material. After one generation this band has disappeared and has been replaced with a band having a density to be expected for equal amounts of N^{14} and N^{15}. Finally, after two generations, *two* bands are observed, one corresponding to 100 per cent N^{14}-DNA and one to the 50:50

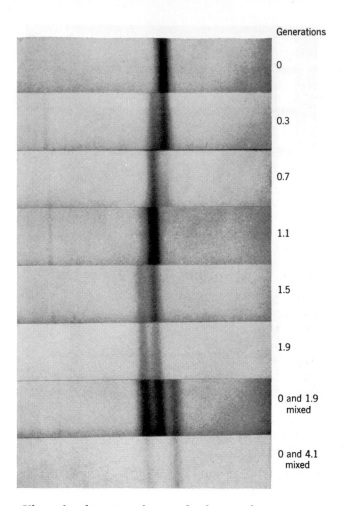

Generations

0

0.3

0.7

1.1

1.5

1.9

0 and 1.9
mixed

0 and 4.1
mixed

Figure 27. Ultraviolet absorption photographs showing the concentration of DNA by density gradient centrifugation of lysates of bacteria sampled at various times after the addition of N^{14} substrates to a growing N^{15}-labeled culture. The length of exposure to N^{14} substrates is indicated in terms of generations. After one generation (fourth frame from the top) the density of the bacterial DNA lies halfway between that of the original N^{15}-labeled material and that of material containing essentially only N^{14} (the left component in the bottom frame). Taken from the work of M. Meselson and F. W. Stahl, *Proc. Soc. Natl. Acad. Sci. U.S.*, **44,** 671 (1958).

N^{14}–N^{15} mixture. In experiments in which cells were permitted to multiply through further generations, the mixed band decreased in amount and was replaced by a greater and greater proportion of the band corresponding to N^{14}-DNA. If replication of DNA had occurred by a process which involved intermediate degradation into smaller pieces with subsequent reutilization of these pieces for the synthesis of new DNA molecules, density of the first-generation molecules could not have corresponded so sharply to a specific equimolar mixture of "light" and "heavy" chains. We would expect, rather, a broad distribution of densities, under such circumstances, quite unlike the results that were actually obtained.

These results are in good agreement with the predictions of the Watson-Crick model. As shown schematically in Figure 28, each strand of the DNA double helix might be visualized as a template on which a new strand is fashioned during replication. If the precursor nucleotides are unlabeled, the two "daughter" helices produced during a single replication would be expected to be half-labeled. After a second replication two strands would be labeled and two unlabeled. Base pairing would assure accurate assembly of complementary strands, and genetic constancy would thus be maintained.

The scheme of base pairing suggested by Watson and Crick has recently received strong support from the enzymatic studies of Arthur Kornberg and his colleagues[18] on the *in vitro* synthesis of DNA-like molecules. They reported, in 1957, that an enzyme had been purified from extracts of *E. coli* which could catalyze the condensation of deoxyribonucleoside triphosphates to form large polydeoxynucleotide chains with the liberation of pyrophosphate in the presence of a DNA "primer." In subsequent studies the enzyme has been purified 4000-fold over the crude extract, and a number of important properties of the system have been delineated. The most dramatic finding has been that the composition of the newly synthesized polymer (having a molecular weight of the order of 5,000,000) exhibits the same purine and pyrimidine base composition as that of the primer, in spite of a constant concentration of each triphosphate added. For example, the addition of DNA from *Aerobacter aerogenes*, having a ratio of adenine plus thymine to guanine plus cytosine of 0.82, induced the formation of "DNA" with a ratio of 0.99. With DNA from T2 coliphage, having a ratio of 1.91, the new material showed a value of 1.98. In keeping with the base pairing of the Watson-Crick model, deoxyuridine triphosphate was incorporated into DNA only in place of thymidine triphosphate and deoxyinosine triphosphate only in place of deoxyguanosine triphosphate. This major break-

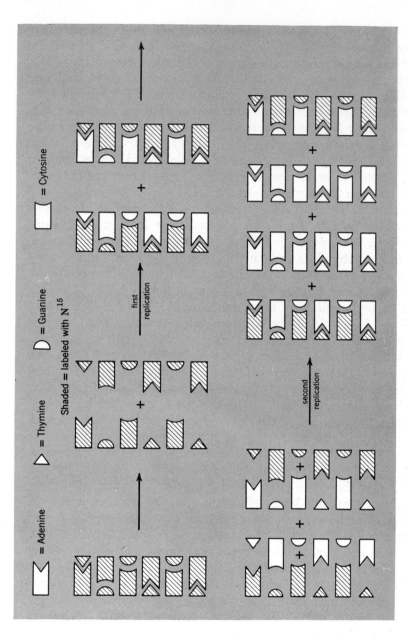

Figure 28. A schematic representation of how the replication of deoxyribonucleic acid might occur. The base sequence in a newly formed strand is determined by the complementarity between adenine and thymine and between guanine and cytosine. A process such as that shown here would be compatible with the results obtained by Meselson and Stahl, some of which are shown in Figure 27.

through, in addition to supplying evidence bearing on DNA structure, may also be a key to the ultimate synthesis of polydeoxynucleotides having specific biological activity.

The studies we have discussed deal with genetic material at the molecular level. To make the results meaningful to biology, they must be shown to apply to, or at least to be consistent with, the behavior of DNA at the level of the organized chromosome. The extrapolation is enormous and consequently entails a good deal of faith. We can determine, for example, that the DNA in a single haploid cell (of *Lilium*) is approximately 53×10^{-12} grams. If we assume that this DNA is present as a single, long double helix, it can be calculated that the length of this coil would be 1.5×10^7 microns, or 15 *meters*, and that the coiled structure would make 4.4×10^9 turns around the screw axis. The mechanical problems of unwinding such a coil during the replication process are of a magnitude to make a picture as simple as this one of no serious value.

In spite of the enormous gaps in knowledge between DNA structure and chromosome organization, recent experiments by Taylor, Woods, and Hughes[19] on chromosome replication make it clear that some hypothesis must be arrived at which will accommodate both chemical and cytological information. Taylor et al. have performed the equivalent of the Meselson-Stahl experiment at the cellular level. Using a technique similar to that employed by Howard and Pelc (page 41), they have studied the distribution of label between daughter cells in successive generations. Their radioautographic technique was made considerably sharper by the use of tritium-labeled thymidine rather than radioactive phosphate as a labeled precursor. Since tritium emits beta particles of rather low energy in comparison with phosphorus, film blackening is more highly localized and the resulting autoradiographs have a high degree of correspondence with cellular structure as observed by microscopic examination.

Vicia faba seedlings were grown in a medium containing tritiated thymidine. During this incubation most of the twelve chromosomes became labeled as evidenced by the correspondence between the location of silver grains in the photographic emulsion and the microscopically visible chromosomes. Roots at this stage were then transferred to nonradioactive thymidine solutions containing colchicine and incubated for varying lengths of time. In the presence of colchicine, *Vicia* chromosomes contract to the metaphase condition and sister chromatids (the two separate strands of the chromosome duplex) are spread apart and are easily observable. Since colchicine

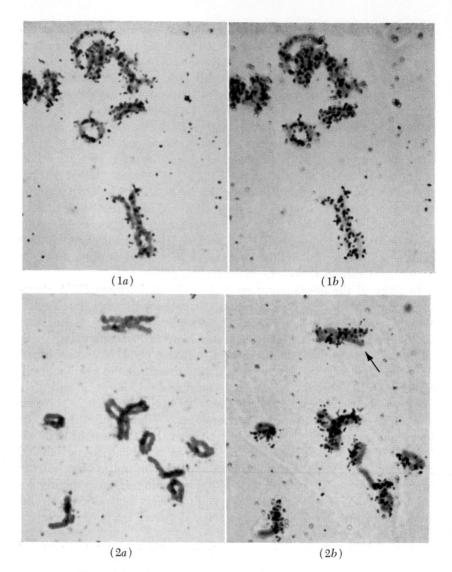

(1a) (1b)

(2a) (2b)

Figure 29. *Vicia faba* chromosomes. Upper half, chromosomes in metaphase, at the first division after labeling with radioactive thymidine: (1a) chromatids spread apart but attached at the centromere; (1b) silver grains in the photographic emulsion above the chromosomes. Lower half, chromosomes after labeling, showing replication in the absence of labeled precursor: (2a) chromosomes from a cell containing 24 chromosomes, with chromatids spread but attached at the centromere; (2b) silver grains in the emulsion above the chromosomes in 2a. As described in the text, these results suggest that the formation of new chromatids takes place at the expense of low molecular weight precursors and does not involve the degradation and reutilization of pre-existing deoxyribonucleic acid.

has the effect of preventing anaphase movements and the subsequent separation of daughter cells, but does not stop chromosomes from duplicating, a count of the number of chromosomal pairs in each cell gives a measure of the number of rounds of replication. Thus, cells with 24 and 48 chromosomes have replicated once and twice, respectively.

Taylor and his colleagues observed that in cells with 24 chromosomes only one of the sister chromatids in each metaphase pair was labeled. It was evident that the pool of labeled precursor had been rapidly depleted in the cells after removal from the initial solution and that replication of chromosomes to yield 24 had involved the use of the nonradioactive thymidine.

In cells with 48 chromosomes, analysis of all 48 was not possible. However, of those that were sufficiently separated for clear observation, approximately half contained one labeled and one unlabeled sister chromatid and half were completely unlabeled. In an occasional "second generation" pair of chromosomes, individual sister chromatids were labeled for only part of their length (see arrow in Figure 29), and in such cases the corresponding portion of the other chromatid showed radioactivity. This behavior is to be expected for crossing over and resembles the cytological observations that have been made for the chromosomes of other species (e.g. the giant salivary gland chromosomes of *Drosophila*).

The results are interpretable in terms of a scheme such as shown in Figure 30. This diagram proposes the presence in each chromosome of two morphological halves held together at the centromere

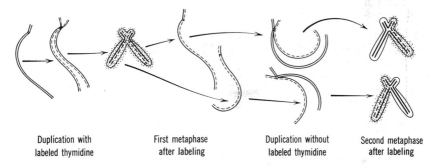

| Duplication with labeled thymidine | First metaphase after labeling | Duplication without labeled thymidine | Second metaphase after labeling |

Figure 30. A schematic representation of the photographs in Figure 29. Solid lines indicate unlabeled units in the chromosome and dashed lines represent radioactive units formed during replication. The dots represent grains in the photographic emulsion caused by radioactive decay of the tritiated thymidine.

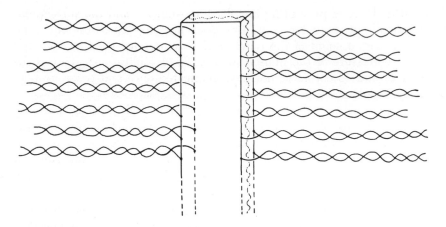

Figure 31. A schematic diagram showing how the chromosome might be organized to account for the results summarized in Figure 29. The chromosome is depicted as consisting of a central core divided into two halves. Each half is attached to one strand of a large number of DNA double helices. Redrawn from J. H. Taylor, *Am. Naturalist*, **91**, 209 (1957).

and containing two equivalent strands. During the initial labeling period each chromatid becomes radioactive, and metaphase figures in cells with twelve chromosomes are uniformly associated with blackening of the emulsion. After a second replication each chromosome pair is still radioactive, but all the radioactivity is associated with the original parent strand and the newly formed strand is unlabeled.*

Realizing the unlikelihood of a double helix running the full length of the chromosome, Taylor, Woods, and Hughes have proposed an interesting model which accommodates both their own radioactive data at the cellular level and the theoretical implications of the double helix. This model (see Figure 31) visualizes the chromosome as composed of two halves, each half consisting of a central core to which is attached one strand of each of a multitude of double helices. When a cell enters the division cycle, the halves separate from one

---

* L. F. La Cour and C. R. Pele have recently repeated these experiments in the *absence* of colchicine and report that radioactivity was distributed between *both* chromatids. No free labeled precursors were present during the period of replication. These results, which are in direct contrast to those of Taylor, Woods, and Hughes, reopen the question of whether replication is, or is not, a completely "conservative" mechanism in which a chromosomal strand, once formed, is retained in the nucleus as an essentially permanent chemical structure.

another, each half carrying with it one of the complementary polynucleotide chains. Taylor and his colleagues point out that the model introduces a new dimension for the interpretation of crossing over. Thus, conventional crossover might occur by exchange along the core, whereas various minor recombinations and gene conversions could occur by interaction or exchange among the side chains of DNA.

Summing up, we may say that a good case can be made for the presence of a set of intertwined helical coils of polynucleotide in DNA. The model proposed by Watson and Crick is, at present, the most satisfactory. Although J. Donohue[20] has shown that certain other arrangements of base pairs can be made which would permit the construction of double-helix models, these do not agree with the X-ray patterns that have been observed for DNA, and the pairing of adenine with thymine and of guanine with cytosine seems most probable at the moment. The complementarity of the two strands forms the basis of an intriguing hypothesis for replication of genetic material, supported by experimental evidence at both the molecular and the cellular level.

Let us now consider briefly some of the bits of evidence that do *not* fit entirely with the Watson-Crick hypothesis. These are not as numerous as the supporting evidence, possibly because scientists, like other citizens, are also attracted to bandwagons.

It has been suggested that the replication of DNA based solely on complementariness of polynucleotide chains might be difficult to reconcile with some of the analytical values for nucleotide abundance. Sinsheimer[9] has isolated a series of dinucleotides from calf thymus DNA (see Table 1) which includes homologous dinucleotides of cytosine and of 5-methylcytosine. The results indicate a considerable difference in the distribution of cytosine and 5-methylcytosine; that is, substitutions do not appear to be random. Although still somewhat preliminary, these findings suggest that simple complementarity might not be an adequate basis for the distribution. There is no obvious stereochemical reason for discrimination against 5-methylcytosine in positions usually occupied by cytosine, and Sinsheimer justifiably recommends that we keep our eyes open for ancillary pathways of nucleotide metabolism or assembly that might explain such deviations from simplicity.

Sinsheimer has also pointed out another more serious objection to simple complementary replication. In T2 bacteriophage, in which cytosine is completely replaced by 5-hydroxymethylcytosine, about 77 per cent of the latter compound occurs conjugated with glucose (see Figure 22). Now various studies (which we shall discuss in the next chapter) have indicated that the DNA of bacteriophage T2 is composed of one large piece comprising about 40 per cent of the total and a number of smaller pieces. All the unconjugated 5-hydroxymethylcytosine is found in the large piece; that is, only about 60 per cent of the large piece is substituted, whereas all the smaller pieces contain glucose. As stated by Sinsheimer, "Since these components of T2 DNA are all replicated in the same cell at the same time, the limited glucose substitution of the large piece cannot reasonably be ascribed to some metabolic limitation. Hence it would appear (to put the matter mechanistically) that when the replication of the large piece takes place, the machinery knows when to put in glucose-substituted 5-hydroxymethylcytosine or when to insert unsubstituted 5-hydroxymethylcytosine, for the glucose content remains unchanged through many generations." These observations could be explained on the basis that 5-hydroxymethylcytosine and its glucose-substituted derivative present, to the assembly line, different stereochemical features which would preclude error in the determination of sequence. The cautions advanced by Sinsheimer concerning simple complimentariness must obviously be kept well in mind, both as brakes on overenthusiasm and for their heuristic value.

Some of the most puzzling evidence contrary to the Watson-Crick-replication hypothesis comes from the work of G. Stent and his co-workers on "suicide" in P^{32}-labeled phage as the result of radioactive decay. These experiments are not easily described, however, without some preliminary consideration of the natural history of bacteriophage; consequently they will be discussed in the following chapter.

Polynucleotide "Codes"

No discussion of DNA in relation to genetics would be complete without some mention of the efforts that have been made to discover a "code" which might permit the translation of base sequence into protein structure. To participate in this game we need have no special knowledge of protein chemistry beyond the following two basic facts: first, proteins consist, for the most part, of polypeptide chains made up of approximately twenty amino acids (*exactly* twenty in codes to date) arranged in a specific sequence for each protein species; and second, the known protein and polypeptide sequences have been assembled in several review articles which are

$$...B C A,\quad C D D,\quad A B A,\quad B D C,...$$

or

$$...B,\quad C A C,\quad D D A,\quad B A B,\quad D C...$$

Figure 32. Linear arrangements of four purine or pyrimidine bases, A,B,C and D, in which triplets, each corresponding to a specific amino acid residue, are separated by commas. The problem is how to read the code if the commas are rubbed out.

easily available in most libraries. Some mathematical facility and considerable imagination are prerequisites.

We shall consider only one such code here, the so-called "comma-less code" of Crick, Griffith, and Orgel.[21] It makes a good example because experimental data have not yet appeared which can rule out this code, and the basic cryptographic approach to "how a sequence of four things [nucleotides] determines a sequence of twenty things [amino acids]" is elegantly illustrated in their paper.

Since there are only four (common) bases, a code founded on correspondence between base *pairs* and amino acid residues would not suffice, only $4 \times 4 = 16$ such pairs being possible. Base *triplets*, on the other hand, are too numerous ($4 \times 4 \times 4 = 64$) without the introduction of restrictions. As one approach to restricting the possibilities, Crick, Griffith, and Orgel have chosen to consider the case of "nonoverlapping codes." An illustration from their discussion states the problem clearly. Letting A, B, C, and D represent the four bases, we may divide a polynucleotide chain of such bases into nonoverlapping triplets, each triplet corresponding to an amino acid residue (Figure 32). "If the ends of the chain are not available, this can be done in more than one way as shown. The problem is how to read the code if the commas are rubbed out, that is, a comma-less code."

The ground rules for this particular coding puzzle were as follows: (1) Some of the 64 triplets make sense, and some "make nonsense"; (2) all the possible sequences of amino acids may occur, and at every point in the string of bases we can only read sense in the correct way. To put ground rule 2 in other words, two triplets that make sense can be put side by side, but overlapping triplets so formed must always be nonsense. Thus, in the sequence ABCDAA, if ABC and DAA make sense, BCD and CDA must always be nonsense.

To prove that 20 is the maximum number of amino acids that can be coded in this manner is quite straightforward. Thus we may

Figure 33. One solution to the problem of how twenty amino acids can be coded by four heterocyclic bases in a "comma-less" code.

eliminate AAA, BBB, etc., since, if in a sequence AAAAAA the triplet AAA corresponds to amino acid *a*, the sequence of six may be misinterpreted by associating acid *a* with the second to fourth, or third to fifth letters. This reduces the 64 possibilities to 60. These 60 may be grouped into twenty sets of three, each set being cyclic permutations of one another. If BCA stands for amino acid *b*, for example, then BCABCA stands for *bb*, and CAB and ABC must be ruled out as nonsense. Since only one triplet can therefore be chosen from each cyclic set, we arrive at the "magic number" of 20.

Having shown that no more than twenty amino acids can be coded by four bases in this system, the authors list a number of solutions, including that shown in Figure 33. The reader may satisfy himself that any two triplets of this set may be placed next to each other without producing overlapping triplets which belong to the set. In all, 288 different solutions were found which conformed to the rules.

If the structure of DNA does, indeed, have some direct relationship to genetic information, we must undoubtedly take into account many structural factors in addition to base sequence, particularly those having to do with the geometrical arrangement of the polynucleotide chain. The business of constructing codes that might have some bearing on the problem of information transfer from DNA to protein is, therefore, mainly of theoretical value at the moment. In time, however, the study of DNA–protein cryptography will undoubtedly become a much more active field. Protein chemists are now beginning to accumulate data relating to the chemical consequences of mutation, and there should soon be a large amount of information for consideration. These data will be, for the most part, very indirect. For example, the single-gene change which leads to the formation of hemoglobin C instead of the normal hemoglobin A is reflected in the replacement of a particular glutamic acid residue by a residue of lysine (Chapter 8). The same replacement has occurred, during evolution, in the ribonuclease molecule where a lysine residue in bovine ribonuclease is replaced by glutamic acid in the sheep protein (Chapter 7). In the first case we can definitely invoke mutation as a causative factor. In the second, mutation is implied but, in view of the impossibility of crossing cows with sheep, a cause and effect relationship cannot be proved. As further examples of this sort accumulate, we shall, perhaps, be able to decide whether there exists some uniform pattern of correspondence between genetic composition and protein structure.

REFERENCES

1. A. Boivin, R. Vendrely, and C. Vendrely, *Compt. rend.*, **226**, 1061 (1948).
2. A. E. Mirsky, in *Genetics in the 20th Century* (L. C. Dunn, editor), Macmillan, New York (1951).
3. S. Zamenhof, R. DeGiovanni, and K. J. Rich, *Bacteriology*, **71**, 60 (1956).
4. A. Howard and S. R. Pelc, *Exptl. Cell Research*, **2**, 178 (1951).
5. O. T. Avery, C. M. MacLeod, and M. McCarty, *J. Exptl. Med.*, **79**, 137 (1944).
6. These studies are reviewed by R. D. Hotchkiss in the book, *The Nucleic Acids*, volume 2 (E. Chargaff and J. N. Davidson, editors), Academic Press, New York, 1955.
7. J. Marmur and R. D. Hotchkiss, *J. Biol. Chem.*, **214**, 383 (1955).
8. Discussed by E. Chargaff in *The Nucleic Acids*, volume 1 (E. Chargaff and J. N. Davidson, editors), Academic Press, New York, 1955.
9. R. L. Sinsheimer, *Science*, **125**, 1123 (1957).
10. H. S. Shapiro and E. Chargaff, *Biochim. et Biophys. Acta*, **26**, 608 (1957).
11. M. H. F. Wilkins, A. R. Stokes, and H. R. Wilson, *Nature*, **171**, 738 (1953).
12. J. D. Watson and F. H. C. Crick, in *Viruses, Cold Spring Harbor Symposia Quant. Biology*, **18**, (1953).
13. L. Pauling and R. B. Corey, *Arch. Biochem. Biophys.*, **65**, 164 (1956).
14. C. A. Thomas, *J. Am. Chem. Soc.*, **78**, 1861 (1956).
15. V. N. Schumaker, E. G. Richards, and H. K. Schachman, *J. Am. Chem. Soc.*, **78**, 4230 (1956).
16. M. Meselson and F. W. Stahl, *Proc. Natl. Acad. Sci. U.S.*, **44**, 671 (1958).
17. M. S. Meselson, F. W. Stahl, and J. Vinograd, *Proc. Natl. Acad. Sci. U.S.*, **43**, 581 (1957).
18. J. Adler, M. J. Bessman, I. R. Lehman, H. K. Schachman, E. S. Simms, and A. Kornberg, *Federation Proc.*, **16**, 153 (1957). See also *Federation Proc.*, **17**, 178 (1958).
19. J. H. Taylor, P. S. Woods, and W. L. Hughes, *Proc. Natl. Acad. Sci. U.S.*, **43**, 122 (1957).
20. J. Donohue, in *Molecular Structure and Biological Specificity*, (L. Pauling and H. Itano, editors), American Institute of Biological Sciences, Publication 2, Washington, D. C., 1957.
21. F. H. Crick, J. S. Griffith, and L. E. Orgel, *Proc. Natl. Acad. Sci. U.S.*, **43**, 416 (1957).

SUGGESTIONS FOR FURTHER READING

Biochemical Society, *The Structure of Nucleic Acids and Their Role in Protein Synthesis,* Cambridge University Press, Cambridge, England, 1957.

The Chemical Basis of Heredity (W. D. McElroy and B. Glass, editors), Johns Hopkins Press, Baltimore, 1957.

Crick, F. H. C., in *Sci. American,* **197,** No. 3, 188 (1957).

Overend, W. G., and A. R. Peacocke, *Endeavour,* **16,** No. 62, 90 (1957).

Taylor, J. H., "The Time and Mode of Duplication of Chromosomes," *Am. Naturalist,* **91,** 209 (1957).

chapter 4

THE SUBSTRUCTURE
OF GENES

As we pointed out in Chapter 1, most evolutionists feel that all levels of evolution can be interpreted in terms of a single basic process, the natural selection of organisms whose phenotypes have been modified in some favorable way by gene mutation. During the earliest stages of evolutionary development, the sudden appearance of new genes must have been a frequent and important occurrence. However, it is, perhaps, not too heretic to suggest that the major proportion of evolution has been the result of a continual process of modification, and integration into new systems of organization, of genetic potentialities already present in our extremely distant ancestors. (We shall consider the evidence for the antiquity of some of our own genes in a later chapter.) Although evolution of the sort undergone by the *Gryphaea* (page 7) is generally referred to as microevolution, such a process is many orders of magnitude more complex than the process that can be demonstrated in favorable test objects like bacteriophages. With bacteriophage we may detect "ultramicroevolutionary" changes caused by even extremely infrequent single-gene mutations. The morphology and general physiology of these most elementary "organisms" are discussed in the following pages, together with a consideration of the progress of "fine-

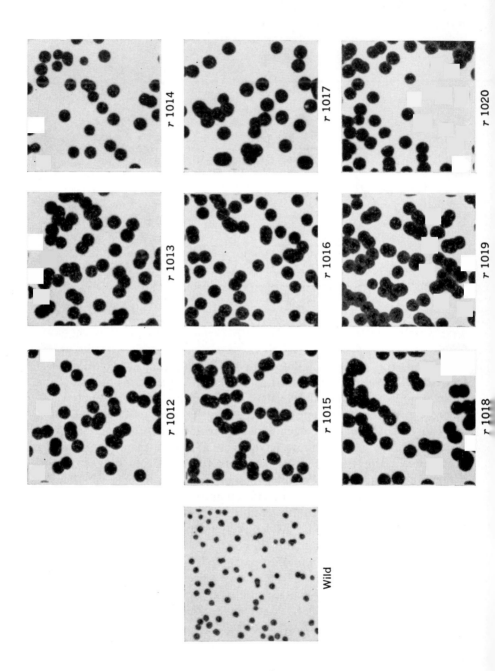

THE MOLECULAR BASIS OF EVOLUTION

structure genetics" which has been so stimulated by work on bacteriophages and on their bacterial cell hosts.

Bacteriophages were discovered by D'Herelle in 1917. He demonstrated that these were extremely small particles, invisible by ordinary microscopy, which multiply parasitically within their host and escape in a burst when the bacterial cell wall ruptures. Later studies by a number of investigators, among whom Delbrück, Demerec, Luria, and Burnet deserve particular mention, showed that the bacteriophage bacterial cell microcosm exhibited many elegant examples of evolutionary adaptation.

A particularly cogent example is presented by the case of the *r* mutants of bacteriophage T4. Each wild-type T4 particle produces a small, fuzzy plaque (Figure 34), when grown on agar containing *E. coli* of strain B. This plaque type is one of the phenotypic characters of this particular phage. From time to time these wild T4 undergo a mutation which introduces a new phenotypic character. Thus we may isolate, from individual plaques of wild T4, mutants that produce quite a different sort of plaque, nine of which are shown in Figure 34. In spite of the identical appearance of plaques produced by all these *r* mutants on *E. coli* B, we may easily distinguish several different sorts of *r* mutants by employing a new bacterial host. Thus, as shown in Figure 35, when the nine *r* mutants are plated on *E. coli* K rather than B, three subgroups become evident; two of the mutants still form *r*-type plaques, one forms wild-type plaques, and six do not multiply at all. Whereas on strain B all the mutants produce a visible effect, on K some are visible (the *r* plaques), some are "innocuous" (wild type), and some are lethal. *Escherichia coli* B, therefore, supplies something which is not supplied by K, at least for the latter *r* mutants. In a sense, K may be thought of as an ecological niche which is not attainable by these "species" of T4 bacteriophages until a mutation has occurred which makes the "something" in B no longer of importance.

◄——

Figure 34. Plaques formed on *E. coli* B by wild-type bacteriophage T4 (left) and by nine independently arising *r* mutants. As described in the text, wild-Type T4 particles infect and multiply within *E. coli* cells of strain B to produce the small plaques shown. The progeny infect and lyse neighboring bacterial cells to produce plaques, which are actually areas in the *E. coli* B–agar mixture that have become translucent owing to lysis of the bacterial suspension; *r* mutants produce the large plaques shown in the nine photographs at the right of the figure. The plaques may easily be distinguished from those produced by the wild-type bacteriophage particles by their characteristic plaque morphology. From S. Benzer, *The Chemical Basis of Heredity*, Johns Hopkins Press, 1957.

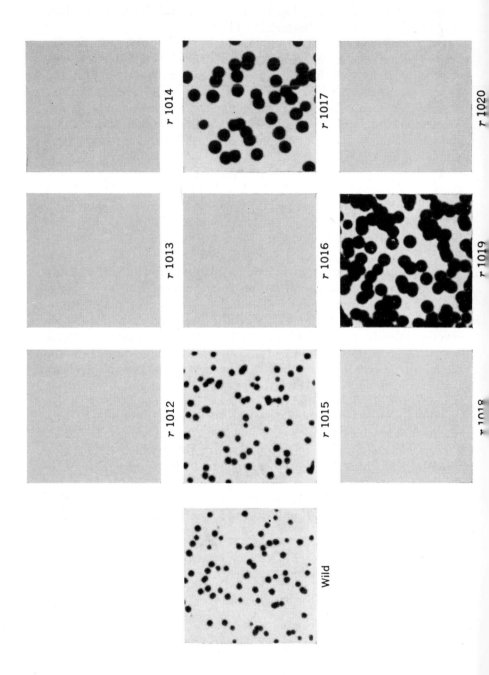

THE MOLECULAR BASIS OF EVOLUTION

Another point of evolutionary interest can be illustrated by these observations. The *r* mutants which *behave* like wild-type phage on *E. coli* K are *not* wild type as is shown by their behavior on B. In terms of evolutionary adaptation, these particles are very much analogous to the reptiles which we discussed in Chapter 1. The reader will recall that changes occurred in the structure of the jaw of reptiles which were not of apparent adaptive value until millions of years later when certain of the bones of the reptilian jaw became important units in the assembly of the characteristic mammalian ear. These changes (call them "aristogenic" if you like) could not be taken advantage of until the proper ecological situations made their presence of great value to the budding mammal. The "false" wild-type phage mutants, in a similar manner, are the possessors of mutations which are, at least superficially, neither "detrimental" nor "advantageous" in a world of *E. coli* K, but which facilitate a marked change in phenotype in a world of *E. coli* B. These *r* mutations might be preserved for a long time, to become of critical importance when environmental (host cell) conditions accidentally changed from K to B. More likely, the abnormal gene would eventually back-mutate to the normal allelic form and be forgotten as an evolutionary ripple.

The Chemistry and Enzymology of Bacteriophages

Although a number of different sorts of bacteriophages have been studied with respect to their chemical composition, morphology, and genetic constitution, we shall restrict our discussion to the so-called T-even (and particularly T2) phages since these have been most commonly chosen for study by virologists and are by far the best understood. These viruses, which infect and kill cells of *E. coli* B, may be divided into major groups on the basis of their ability or inability to invade *E. coli* B cells of certain types. Thus *E. coli* B6 will support growth of T2 and T4 viruses, B4 will support T2 and T6 but not T4, and so on. They may be further distinguished on the basis of their plaque morphology, the rate at which such plaques

◄ ————————————————————————————————————

Figure 35. When the nine *r* mutants, shown in Figure 34, are plated on *E. coli* K rather than on strain B, three subgroups become distinguishable. Two mutants continue to form plaques similar to those formed on *E. coli* B, one forms wild-type plaques, and six do not multiply at all. From S. Benzer, *The Chemical Basis of Heredity*, Johns Hopkins Press, 1957.

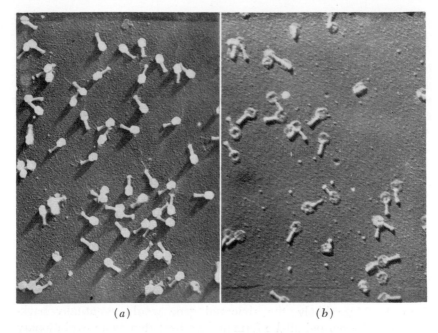

(a)   (b)

Figure 36. Electron photomicrographs of (a) bacteriophage T2 and of (b) "ghosts" prepared by osmotic shock. These photographs were obtained through the kindness of Dr. Roger Herriott. From R. M. Herriott and J. L. Barlow. *J. Gen. Physiol.*, **40**, 809 (1957).

become visible under standard conditions of agar plate culture, and their specific serological characteristics.

The virus particles can be visualized in the electron microscope, and the morphology of T2 coliphage, which is more or less typical for all the T phages, is shown in Figure 36. The particles are made up of a rounded hexagonal head and a tail. The tip of the tail is slightly expanded into a knob-like structure. This can be deduced from the outlines of some of the shadows in the electron micrograph.

Intact phage particles consist of approximately 60 per cent protein and 40 per cent DNA, together with traces of lipid material. The nucleic acid component is entirely of the DNA variety and, as discussed earlier, contains the unusual pyrimidine 5-hydroxymethylcytosine partly in glucosidic combination with glucose. It was believed for some time that the DNA and protein were tightly conjugated in nucleoprotein form. It can be shown, however, that the DNA is actually physically enclosed within a protein shell, the so-called bacteriophage "ghost," and can be released from the interior of the particle by suitable treatment, whereupon it becomes digestible by deoxyribonuclease. In Figure 36 is shown a collection of such ghosts which have been prepared by submitting virus particles to "osmotic shock," that is, rapid dispersion into distilled water after prior equilibration with strong salt solution. The ghosts may be prepared in a form essentially devoid of polynucleotide by proper washing. The separability of protein and DNA is elegantly demonstrated by the fact that, when phages are doubly labeled with P^{32} and S^{35}, the P^{32} is found entirely in the DNA released by "shock" and the S^{35} in the material of the ghosts.

Doubly labeled phage have also been used by Hershey and Chase to study the fate of the various components of phage during infection and rupture of bacterial cells. These investigators allowed the labeled particles to infect *E. coli* cells and, after a brief period, exposed the mixture to rapid agitation in a Waring Blendor. The P^{32}-labeled DNA was found entirely within the infected bacterial cells, whereas a large part of the protein was sheared off. The small amount of S^{35}-labeled protein which adhered to the bacterial cells after the agitation procedure did not contribute to the structure of the progeny phage produced when the infected cells were allowed to incubate and rupture spontaneously. Since the infected cells which were exposed to the blender produced a normal yield of progeny, it may be concluded that DNA alone is capable of directing the synthesis of new particles, genotypically identical with the parent phage, and that the protein shell around the DNA makes no contribution to the process of genetic information transfer. Although lacking any genetic role, the protein ghost is responsible for many features of bacteriophage infection in addition to its function as an enclosure for DNA. Ghosts can attach to compatible host cells or cell walls, that is, they bear the host specificity of the intact virus (see Chapter 8). Cells which have been "infected" with ghosts are killed and subsequently lyse, although no progeny phage are produced. Ghosts also have the mysterious ability to cause inhibition of RNA synthesis and protein synthesis within the host cell.

It has been known for some time that small molecular fragments of the bacterial cell wall are released shortly after infection by an enzyme present in both intact viruses and ghosts. This material has been identified as a mucopeptide derivative having the interesting structure shown in Figure 37. Now, although the nature of the natural substrate for the enzyme, lysozyme, is not known with precision, a number of observations suggest that the function of lysozyme is to attack mucopolysaccharide or mucoprotein compounds. It will degrade chitin, for example, which is a long-chained poly-N-acetyl glucosamine, although it will not attack this substance after de-

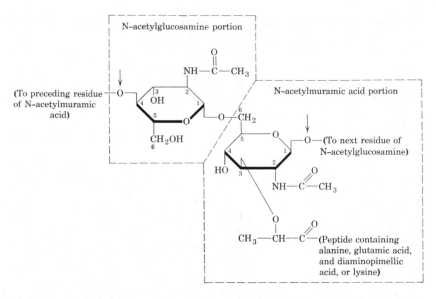

Figure 37. A proposed structure for the fragment which is produced from the cell walls of certain Gram-positive bacteria by digestion with lysozyme. The arrows indicate the probable site of attack by the enzyme. Redrawn from W. Brumfitt, A. C. Wardlaw, and J. T. Park, *Nature*, **181**, 1783 (1958).

acetylation. The chemical nature of the fragment split off from the cell wall is sufficiently reminiscent of chitin to suggest that the viral enzyme responsible for bacterial penetration is, indeed, of the lysozyme variety. Dreyer and Koch[1] have recently compared the action of crystalline egg white lysozyme and virus ghosts on bacterial cell walls and have found that a very similar cleavage product is released by both catalytic agents. Further, the enzymatic activity in the ghosts distributes in the same way as the egg white enzyme during purification with the specific adsorbent, Bentonite, and can be chromatographed on the ion exchange resin, XE-64, to give a similar elution pattern. Chemical comparison of the two lysozymes has not yet been made, so we cannot state categorically that the virus enzyme has structural features in common with the egg white enzyme. The chromatographic properties and similar molecular size of the phage enzyme (slowly dialyzable through cellophane membranes) makes this similarity rather likely, however, and sequential analysis should give very interesting results. It will be of obvious importance, in connection with the "age" of genes and with the evolutionary process in general, to determine whether or not an enzyme designed to digest cell wall material is an essential component even in "semi-living" biological systems like the coliphages.

Morphology of T Phages

Some idea of the number of morphological components making up the bacteriophage particle may be obtained by electron microscopic

Figure 38. An electron photomicrograph of a crude lysate of bacteriophage T2 prepared by treatment of infected *E. coli* cells with chloroform. The photograph shows intact bacteriophage particles and a collection of "heads," rods, and filaments. This photograph was obtained through the kindness of Dr. E. Kellenberger of the University of Geneva.

THE SUBSTRUCTURE OF GENES

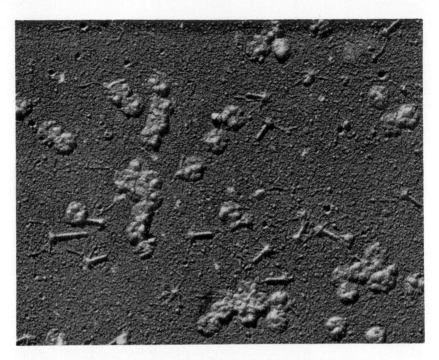

Figure 39. An electron photomicrograph of partially purified rods from the lysate shown in Figure 38. Many of these rods may be seen to terminate in a brush-like arrangement. This photograph was obtained through the kindness of Dr. E. Kellenberger of the University of Geneva.

examination of a phage which has been subjected to various degradative treatments (peroxide, cadmium cyanide, N-ethylmaleimide) which split off from the body of the phage certain parts of the tail structure. We may also examine the contents of artificially lysed bacterial cells which are still in the process of synthesizing phage. The electron micrograph shown in Figure 38, for example, was made by Kellenberger and Sechaud on the crude lysate of T2 prepared by treatment of infected *E. coli* cells with chloroform. The photograph shows, in addition to intact phages, a collection of empty heads, rods, and filaments, the latter very likely being strands of DNA which have not yet been wrapped in their protein envelope. These phage components may be concentrated as shown in Figure 39. The rods, which must constitute a large part of the tail structure, are seen in many cases to terminate in a wire-brush-like arrangement. In some electron micrographs we can distinguish rod-like structures which are somewhat smaller in diameter than the intact viral tail and which have been interpreted as a sort of plug in the tail which confines the DNA to the head of the phage. Two other phage components, not visualized by the electron microscope, are the penetration enzyme (lysozyme?) and the protein material responsible for host range specificity. The latter may be associated with one of the morphologically distinguishable tail components.

The drawing in Figure 40 summarizes, in a schematic way, the subunits of structure which have been detected microscopically. A slightly different reconstruction has been proposed by Kozloff, Lute, and Henderson.[2] This diagram helps to point out one of the major puzzles of bacteriophage biosynthesis, namely, the problem of how the DNA strand or strands are gotten into the preformed heads, if these are indeed synthesized before DNA is. We might visualize that either an enzyme system, rich in genetic information, is able to

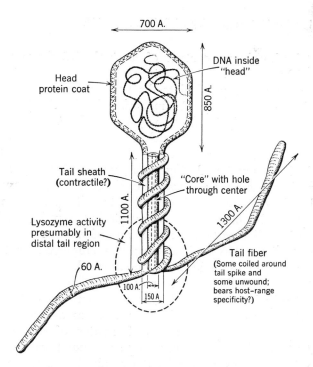

Figure 40. A schematic reconstruction of the morphology of a bacteriophage particle. The dimensions shown are approximate and are averaged from several sources (see, for example, the excellent work of R. C. Williams and D. Fraser, *Virology*, **2**, 289 (1956).

carry out DNA synthesis within the head (perhaps in cooperation with the protein of the head itself) or that DNA can thread itself into the head after synthesis on the outside. The possibility must not be overlooked, however, that phage fragments really represent abortive attempts at synthesis and that the protein shell and tail of completed phage particles are assembled around a preformed mass of DNA. The latter possibility is supported by a certain amount of experimental evidence and certainly makes the best sense, metabolically and mechanically. For example, Hershey has shown with isotopic tracer methods that the DNA of phage is synthesized before the protein precursors and that the small amount of protein synthesis which occurs before DNA synthesis may form some essential enzymes (perhaps for the synthesis of the unique pyrimidine, or for the formation of a ribonucleic acid "template") which are not otherwise present in the bacterial host.

The Molecular Heterogeneity of Coliphage DNA

The total phosphorus content of a single T2-phage particle is about 2×10^{-17} grams. If all this phosphorus resides in a single DNA molecule, we may calculate the total molecular weight of this DNA to be approximately 110 million. Should the Watson-Crick type of structure apply in phage, we are faced with the problem of how each enormously long polynucleotide strand becomes replicated during phage multiplication and how the two intertwined strands in the double helix unwind during, or in preparation for, this event.

This problem has been somewhat simplified by the observations of Levinthal and Thomas.[3] Their experiments indicate that the DNA of phage may not be in a single large unit but may be made up of a number of smaller parts, the largest one of which makes up about 40 per cent of the DNA. The technique employed by them is a particularly elegant example of simplicity combined with sensitivity and precision. Levinthal and Thomas embedded bacteriophage particles, previously labeled with P^{32}, in an electron-sensitive emulsion in which the passage of fast electrons, such as are emitted by P^{32} during radioactive decay, causes the formation of a track of silver grains. A single phage particle, acting as a "point source," can thus cause the formation of a "star" in the emulsion, each arm of which is produced by the decay of a single atom of phosphorus within the DNA of the particle (Figure 41). The sensitivity of the detecting method is such that the radioactivity of a phage particle, emitting

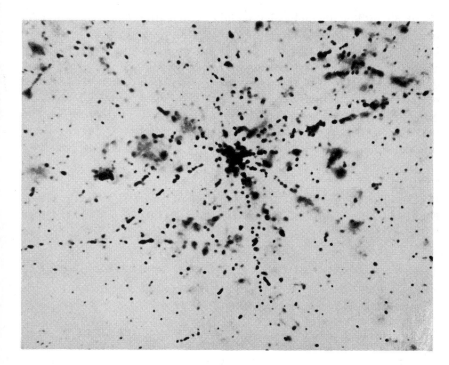

Figure 41. Photomicrograph of a "star" produced by radioactive decay of labeled phosphorus within the DNA of a phage particle embedded in a photographic emulsion. This photograph was obtained through the kindness of Professor Cyrus Levinthal, Massachusetts Institute of Technology.

only about fifteen disintegrations per month, can be estimated. In uniformly labeled electron sources (e.g. the DNA of a single phage particle or fragments thereof) the number of tracks per star gives a measure of the molecular size of the emitting source, relative to the intact phage particle.

The number of tracks per star was determined for intact phage and for first- and second-generation progeny before and after osmotic shock. The results for the various fractions are shown in Table 2, expressed in terms of the number of P^{32} atoms in the star-forming particle, normalized to 100 for the original uniformly labeled phage. (Put in another way, if each star formed by intact parent phage particles has 100 tracks, each star produced by particles in suspensions of "shocked" phage, having half the content of DNA, will show 50 tracks.) The results indicate that (a) there is a single large piece of DNA comprising about 40 per cent of the total DNA (i.e., about 45 million in molecular weight), (*b*) after one generation in nonradioactive bacteria there are, among the progeny, a few particles in which this large piece of DNA has approximately half the P^{32} atoms of the large piece in the parent phage, and (*c*) after a *second* generation the size of this large piece does not change (the same number of tracks per star is observed). Since some 100 to 200 progeny are formed from each parental phage, the *number* of labeled particles in second generation shockates was too few to permit accurate detection and track counting.

TABLE 2
The Number of Arms per "Star" for Various Suspensions of Intact or Ruptured Phage Particles, Normalized to 100 for the Original, Intact Particles[3]

	Intact Phage	After Osmotic Shock
Uniformly labeled parental phage	100	40 ± 4
First-generation progeny	24 ± 3	23 ± 3
Second-generation progeny	26 ± 3	Too dilute for study

The simplest and most appealing interpretation of these data is that the large piece represents the "chromosome" of the phage and that the two halves of its double helical structure serve as templates for the synthesis of new DNA in the progeny. This wishful picture is completely analogous to the scheme growing out of the Meselson and Stahl experiments on *E. coli* DNA. There is, however, no compelling evidence to indicate that the DNA of the T phages is in the form of a double helix, although this is generally assumed in most discussions of the subject for the obvious reason that it makes discussion possible.

The Levinthal-Thomas experiments suggest a "conservative" mechanism of replication during which the structure of the large piece of DNA is not degraded or involved in exchange with external sources of nucleotides.

It would have been pleasant, in connection with this discussion of these experiments, to have been able to present some evidence for the chromosome-like nature of the "big piece." Attempts have been made to show that, during the production of progeny phage, genetic markers, chosen at random along the genetic strand, always accompany the large star-forming fragment. The early experiments along

THE MOLECULAR BASIS OF EVOLUTION

this line looked quite encouraging but, of late, the picture has become rather murky and, after consultation with some of the investigators in the field, it appears that the subject is best avoided at the present time. There are, for example, several lines of evidence which suggest rather strongly that the "40 per cent piece" is *not* a single molecule but that various mild treatments can cause this aggregate to dissociate into still smaller units having molecular weights in the neighborhood of 12 to 15 million. The results of the original "star" experiments seem to be unequivocal and, indeed, chromatographic separation on special columns of ion exchange resin have also shown the presence in T2 DNA of an entity containing about 40 per cent of the total phosphorus. Nevertheless, any attempt to relate the chemical structure of phage DNA to genetic behavior must be deferred until much more data have been obtained.

The Life Cycle and Biosynthesis of T Phages

It may be useful at this point to consider the events that occur following infection of *E. coli* with T phages. Most of the metabolic consequences of infection are summarized in Figure 42, which is a slightly modified form of that given by R. Hotchkiss in his excellent review of 1954, and in Figure 43, taken from an article by L. Kozloff in the *Cold Spring Harbor Symposia* for 1953. Figure 42 gives a condensed view of the fates of various morphological components of the infecting phage and the host cell and also indicates, in a rough way, the manner in which the metabolism of the combined DNA, protein, and ribonucleic acids of the infected cell is altered. It is assumed that the RNA of the host is, in some way, involved in the biosynthesis of phage protein. This assumption is based on certain general observations on protein synthesis which we shall discuss in more detail in Chapter 10.

Kozloff's pictorial summary of the origins of phage DNA and protein (Figure 43) emphasizes that the major share of phage protein is derived from the nutrient medium. Of the newly synthesized phage DNA, it would appear that most of the phosphorus is also exogenous in origin, but that a considerable amount of host DNA is reutilized as a source of purines and pyrimidines.

The kinetics of the various metabolic processes that commence after phage infection are of particular importance in connection with the elucidation of the way in which the genetic information in phage DNA is translated into the chemical structure of progeny phage.

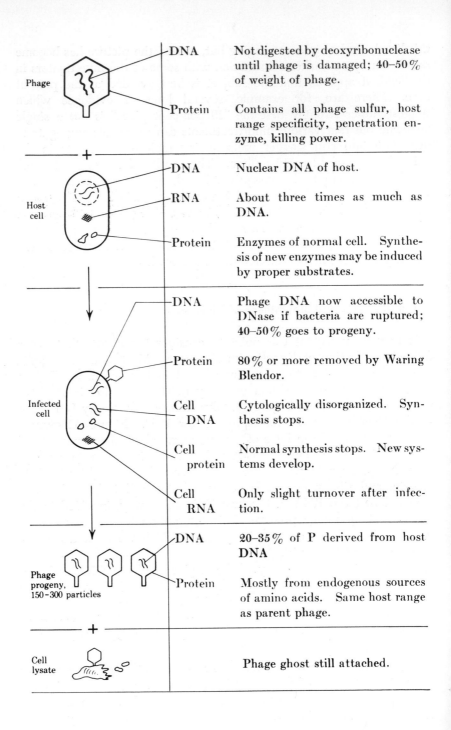

Phage	DNA	Not digested by deoxyribonuclease until phage is damaged; 40–50% of weight of phage.
	Protein	Contains all phage sulfur, host range specificity, penetration enzyme, killing power.
+		
Host cell	DNA	Nuclear DNA of host.
	RNA	About three times as much as DNA.
	Protein	Enzymes of normal cell. Synthesis of new enzymes may be induced by proper substrates.
Infected cell	DNA	Phage DNA now accessible to DNase if bacteria are ruptured; 40–50% goes to progeny.
	Protein	80% or more removed by Waring Blendor.
	Cell DNA	Cytologically disorganized. Synthesis stops.
	Cell protein	Normal synthesis stops. New systems develop.
	Cell RNA	Only slight turnover after infection.
Phage progeny, 150–300 particles	DNA	20–35% of P derived from host DNA
	Protein	Mostly from endogenous sources of amino acids. Same host range as parent phage.
+		
Cell lysate		Phage ghost still attached.

When the host cell becomes infected, its metabolic machinery appears to become completely devoted to phage synthesis. Protein synthesis goes on but produces a new set of proteins. After a short delay, DNA synthesis proceeds actively. However, if the initial protein synthesis is prevented by the addition of a suitable inhibitor such as chloramphenicol, the synthesis of DNA does not take place. On the other hand, if the inhibitor is added *after* protein synthesis has gotten under way, DNA synthesis *can* proceed. These observations suggest that an essential set of enzymes must first be formed, perhaps for the synthesis of the unique 5-hydroxymethylcytosine or its glucose conjugate, before DNA assembly is possible.

Stent and his colleagues have carried out interesting experiments[4] which have a direct bearing on the problem of the order of events during information transfer. They infected P^{32}-labeled cells with P^{32}-labeled phage, both having a sufficiently high level of isotope to cause chemical modification of a significant fraction of the DNA when the phosphorus atoms decayed to form sulfur atoms. The infected cells were incubated in a P^{32} medium so that the progeny phage were also heavily labeled. Samples of infected cells were frozen at $-196°C$. at various times after infection and were stored in this state of suspended animation. During this time P^{32} decay took place. The surprising result was obtained that, in those samples frozen approximately 10 minutes after infection, there was no detectable change in the ability of the infected cells to produce infective phage progeny in spite of the destruction of a considerable portion of the DNA by radioactive "suicide." The results have been interpreted in several ways, the most provocative being the hypothesis that, early in the synthesis of progeny, information in the DNA of the infecting phage particle is transferred to some substance, perhaps protein in nature, which is not susceptible to radioactive decay. Another speculation which could explain the results would require that the structure of DNA be such that, in spite of occasional breaks in the sugar-phosphate backbone of the molecule caused by P^{32} decay, hydrogen bonds hold the macromolecule intact and in a configuration adequate for purposes of replication (Figure 44).

The possible conflicts in logic that might arise from a comparison of the P^{32}-decay data with the experiments of Levinthal and Thomas or with the mass of evidence supporting the central role of a specific

◀ ───

Figure 42. The course of infection of *E. coli* with bacteriophages of the T series. Redrawn after R. D. Hotchkiss, *The Nucleic Acids,* volume 2, Academic Press, 1954.

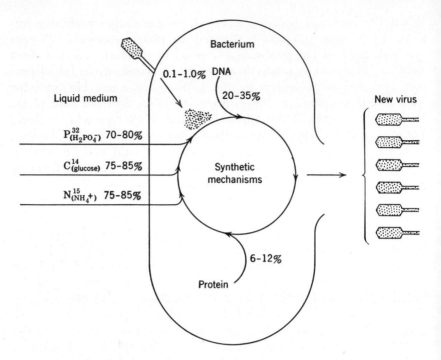

Figure 43. Schematic representation of the origin of the phosphorus, nitrogen, and carbon of bacteriophages T2, T4, and T6. Percentages show origin of material found in viral offspring. Redrawn from L. N. Kozloff, *Cold Spring Harbor Symposia Quan. Biol.*, **18**, 209 (1953).

DNA structure in the determination of heredity are not, to my knowledge near resolution. Fortunately for the following discussion of genetics in phage, we do not need an answer to the fascinating problem of phage replication. Although the behavior of phage during "mating" may only superficially resemble the process as it occurs in more respectable organisms, the phenomena of recombination and segregation, and of linkage, are exhibited in qualitatively the same way.

Genetic Mapping in Bacteriophage

In most organisms it is not possible to construct a single gene map, but instead we find that the various genes fall into several linkage groups (see Chapter 2). However, in bacteriophage T4 and T2, for which quite a few "genes" have been mapped, only a single linkage group seems to be present, and these phages behave genetically as an organism with a single haploid chromosome. The sort of gene map obtained depends, naturally, on the strain of bacteria chosen as host. As we have already shown, the plaque characteristics of mutants that are *r* type on *E. coli* B may be quite different when the mutants are plated in *E. coli* K. The map obtained with a particular host cell, therefore, includes only the loci that cause a detectable change in phenotype in this chosen environment.

The construction of a genetic map for bacteriophage involves more or less the same manipulations that have been used for such organisms as *Drosophila* or peas. A wild-type strain is chosen arbi-

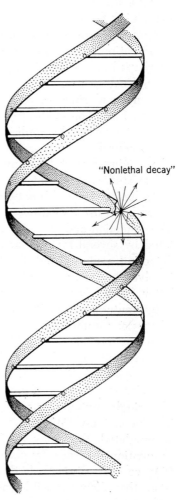

"Nonlethal decay"

Figure 44. A schematic representation of how breaks in the chains of the DNA dougle helix, caused by radioactive decay of P[32], might occur and still permit the maintenance of a relatively intact structure through the forces of hydrogen bonding between complementary pairs of purine and pyrimidine bases.

trarily. Mutants are then chosen on the basis of some easily recognized phenotypic character such as plaque morphology on a particular strain of *E. coli*. The relative position of two mutant loci on the "chromosome" of the phage may then be established by "mating" the mutants and observing the proportion of the progeny that differ from the two parental mutants. True mating does not, of course, occur with phage. Instead, bacterial cells are mixedly infected with the two phages in question, and recombination is allowed to take place within the cell by some obscure process that has the superficial characteristics of crossing over in higher organisms. As we discussed earlier, conventional crossing over results in the production of the two possible recombinants, the wild type and the double recombinant containing both mutant loci. It has been shown that, in phage, such reciprocal crossover does not take place, but that in any single recombination event only one or the other recombinant is formed [perhaps because of a "copy-choice" replication (Figure 45)]. However, since a single phage particle gives rise to several hundred progeny, and since there appears to be about the same probability for the formation of the two kinds of recombinants, the usual statistical treatment may be applied.

Seymour Benzer[4] has, over the past few years, been in the process of mapping a very large number of *r* mutants of bacteriophage T4. These studies represent the first real attempt to determine the ultimate limits of recombination and involve "running the map into the ground," to use an expression attributed by Benzer to Max Delbrück. The detection and mapping of mutations in bacteriophages are facilitated by several factors, including the sensitivity of the technique for detecting mutants and the occurrence of certain mutations which involve the "deletion" of a considerable portion of the map. The latter factor, as we shall see, has permitted Benzer to group many point mutations into "families," thus greatly decreasing the number of crosses required.

In any population of T4 there occurs from time to time a spontaneous mutation which leads to the production of an *r*-type plaque on *E. coli* B agar plates. Since an astronomical number of phage particles may be plated on a single Petri dish surface, the presence of a single mutant in as many as 10^9 particles is easily observed by its *r* phenotype. When a suitable number of such mutants has been accumulated, they may be further subdivided into three subgroups as mentioned earlier, by plating on *E. coli* K. By this trick (see page 69) we may distinguish those that still show *r* morphology on K, those that show the wild-type phenotype, and those that fail to grow

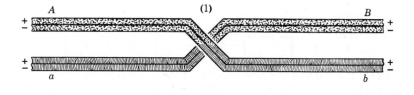

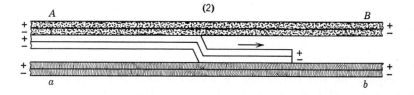

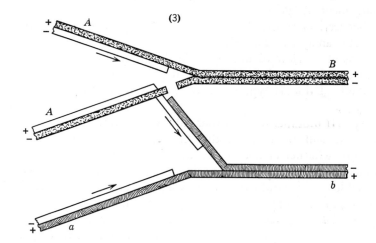

Figure 45. Three possible mechanisms of genetic recombination: *A* and *B* represent two genetic loci and *a* and *b* their alleles. (1) Fragmenting crossing over; the two parental duplexes synapse and break between the loci in question, and heterologous pieces rejoin. (2) Nonfragmenting copy choice. (3) Fragmenting copy choice; parent duplexes unwind and semiconservative replication occurs along the single strands. A switchover occurs between loci *A* and *B* as the parent chains break, and the daughter chains continue to grow complementary to a single chain of the second duplex. Redrawn from M. Delbrück and G. Stent *The Chemical Basis of Heredity,* Johns Hopkins Press, 1957.

Figure 46. The order of the three subunits of the *r* region in the genetic material of bacteriophage T4. Since *r*II and *r*III are farther apart than *r*II and *r*I, the frequency of recombination between *r*II and *r*III mutants should be greater than that between *r*II and *r*I mutants.

at all. These three groups, termed the *r*I, *r*II, and *r*III categories, respectively, may be arranged in the proper linear order by performing mixed-infection crosses. As may be deduced from the scheme in Figure 46, the frequency of recombination between members of the *r*II and *r*III groups would be greater than between mutants of the *r*II and *r*I varieties, making the usual assumption of a linear arrangement of "genes."

Benzer has chosen to concentrate mainly on the *r*II region for his genetic analysis. The *r*II mutants have one clear advantage from the point of view of detection, in that they do not grow on K at all and therefore give an unequivocal phenotypic test. Some thousand mutants of the *r*II type could thus easily be selected for the mapping project.

The *r*II mutants were further subdivided on the basis of the *cis-trans* test. It will be recalled that this genetic trick enables us to determine whether or not two mutants which show a similar phenotypic abnormality are concerned with the same functional unit of heredity or with two separate functions which interact, cooperatively, in producing the change. As we discussed in connection with the "lozenge" genes of *Drosophila* (Chapter 2), three closely linked genetic loci all appeared to be part of the same functional unit since crosses between double heterozygotes bearing both mutant loci on the *same* strand of the chromosome duplex (i.e., in the *cis* arrangement) produced wild-type recombinants, whereas crosses between double heterozygotes in the *trans* arrangement did not. The adequacy of the *cis* arrangement was explained on the assumption that the one, unmarred, strand of the chromosome supplied the required unit of physiological function in sufficient quantity to satisfy the needs of the organism even in the presence of one "nonfunctional" chromatid.

In phage, although the genetic material behaves as though the organism were haploid, the *cis-trans* test can still be applied since mixed infection with two mutants appears to simulate the more conventional diploid situation in higher organisms. Thus, when a mutant

THE MOLECULAR BASIS OF EVOLUTION

phage containing an *r* mutation is introduced into an *E. coli* K host cell along with a wild-type phage particle, the cells are lysed and both kinds of parent phage are liberated. The presence of the wild-type presumably supplies the function missing in the *r* mutant (the *r*II mutation is "recessive"). Although the test has not been made, it is also assumed that mixed infection with a wild type, and with a double *r* mutant bearing both mutations on the same strand, would permit the formation of both sorts of progeny, and for the same reason. When two *r* mutants are used, however, lysis of host cells and progeny production will take place only if the two mutants are deficient in *different functional units*. The various situations are schematized in Figure 47. When two *r* mutants fail to lyse *E. coli* K following mixed infection, the mutations are said to belong to the same "cistron" (the name derived from the test employed). When they supplement one another and cause lysis, they are said to belong to different cistrons. By this sort of technique, Benzer divided the *r*II mutants into two functionally different groups which he names the A and B cistrons (Figure 48). (We might visualize that each of the various phage-synthesizing enzymes, whose formation is induced in bacteria by phage infection, is represented by a different cistron.)

Now it is clear that to map a large number of mutant loci, even after such further subdivision, would require an impossible number of crosses, and Benzer has taken advantage of the fact that some of the mutations appear to involve a change in much more than a point locus. These unusual mutations are detected by the fact that, when

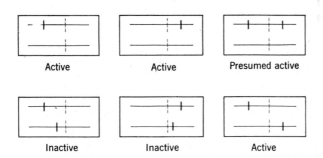

Active   Active   Presumed active

Inactive   Inactive   Active

Figure 47. Schematic diagram showing the results of *cis* and *trans* configurations of double "heterozygotes" bearing two *r*II mutations. *Active* means extensive lysis of the doubly infected cells. *Inactive* means very little lysis. The presence of one "unmarred" strand is pictured as being sufficient to supply the required unit of physiological function.

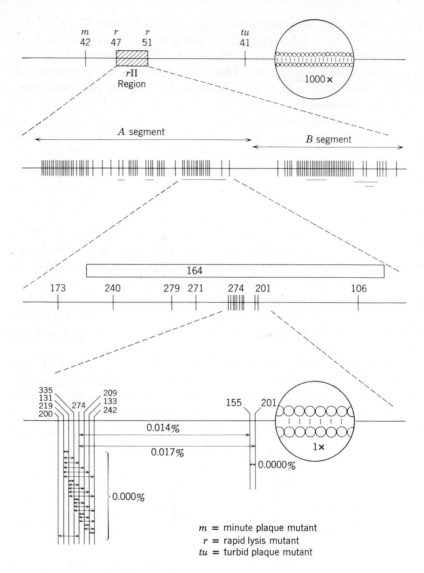

Figure 48. A partial linkage map of T4 bacteriophage. The successive drawings indicate increasing orders of magnification of the *r*II region as revealed by the fine-structure analysis of this region. This figure is highly schematic, and for details of its construction the reader should consult the article by S. Benzer in "Mutation," *Brookhaven Symposia in Biol.*, No. 8 (1956). Redrawn by permission of the author.

they are crossed with several other mutants which give wild-type recombinants when crossed with one another, no detectable wild-type recombinants are observed. The situation is explainable on the basis of the chart shown in Figure 49. If mutant 6 represents a "deletion" type of mutation, and 1 through 5 represent various other ordinary point mutations, crosses between 6 and either 2, 3, or 4 will not yield wild-type recombinants since 6 is deficient in the same properties that are missing in the other three. Wild-type recombinants *could*, however, be obtained from crosses between 6 and either of 1 and 5 since there is no overlap. Using "deletion" mutants for further screening within each of the two cistrons, Benzer was able to simplify the task of mapping since it was then necessary to perform crosses in all combinations only with the mutants that fell within any given deletion region, rather than with *all* the mutants in each cistron. We shall not describe, in detail, this part of the mapping project. In spite of the shortcuts devised, the job was obviously extremely laborious. The schematic map shown in Figure 50 was constructed from crossover data obtained on some of the 923 *r* mutants and shows, in addition to the location of "point" mutations, the location of various of the deletion mutants (the horizontal bars or lines) which were of such value in mapping. The map also

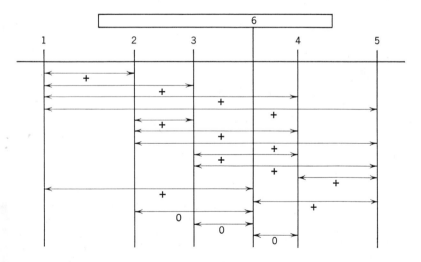

Figure 49. Schematic diagram showing the behavior of an "anomalous" mutant. Mutant 6 fails to give wild-type recombinants with mutants 2, 3 and 4 located within the same segment of the genetic strand. Wild-type recombinants are given, however, with 1 and 5.

THE SUBSTRUCTURE OF GENES 91

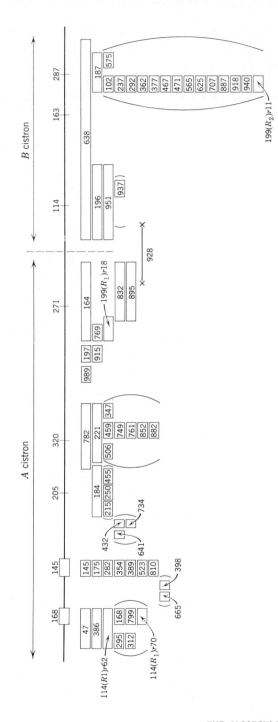

Figure 50. A genetic map showing the locations of a number of *r*II mutants. Some regions of the genetic material appear to be "hot spots," and at such localities a large series of mutants may be isolated, all of which are probably at the same locus (e.g. the series which begins with 102). Parentheses indicate groups in which internal order was not established. To appreciate this map properly the reader should consult the article by S. Benzer in *The Chemical Basis of Heredity*, Johns Hopkins Press, 1957.

THE MOLECULAR BASIS OF EVOLUTION

incorporates the observation, made by Benzer, that a great many separate mutations turn out to be in *the same* location. In other words, some regions of the genetic material of the *r*II zone appeared to possess a much higher mutability than others. The word "appeared" is used advisedly since it must be remembered that the detectability of a mutant depends on the phenotypic test. We have seen, for example, that some *r* mutants behave on *E. coli* K as though the mutation were lethal to the phage in this environment. Others behave like wild-type phage. These classes are, of course, not associated with the *r*II region as was just discussed. However, we may postulate (and the postulation is supported in part by certain observations which we shall discuss in Chapter 6) that the substances whose synthesis is controlled by one or the other of the two cistrons in the *r*II region contain some structural features of greater importance than others. A mutation leading to modifications in the functionally less critical parts of structure in a phenotypic protein might be much less frequently detected since its influence on the "*r*-ness" of an *r* mutant growing on K might be slight in comparison with the effects of the mutations that cause a complete inability to grow on K; that is, those that have caused modifications in the chemistry of a phenotypic protein of a magnitude which completely abolishes function.

The *cistron*, conceived of by Benzer as the genetic unit of function, is clearly a very sophisticated structure. It contains many distinguishable genetic subunits as is indicated by the number of individual loci, within its length, that can be detected by recombination. Benzer, who like Levinthal is a converted physicist, has coined names for the operational subunits within the cistron that have a delightfully physical ring. The *recon* is defined as the smallest element in the one-dimensional array that is interchangeable, but not divisible, by recombination. The *muton* is defined as the smallest element of the cistron that, when altered, gives rise to a mutant form of the organism.

The size of the recon can be estimated by isolating and mapping so large a number of mutants within any given region that the distance between individual points on the map begin to approach the indivisible unit. The recon is thus an empirical unit smaller than or is equal to the smallest nonzero interval between pairs of mutants. The length of the muton is determined by estimating the discrepancy in map distances between closely linked sets of mutants. As shown in Figure 51, the "length" of mutation 2 is equal to the discrepancy between the long distance and the sum of the two short dis-

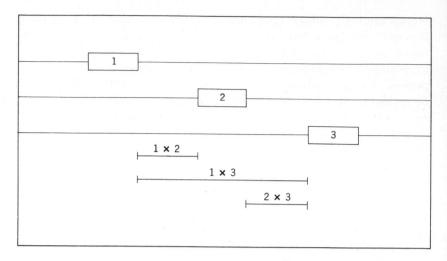

Figure 51. Determining the "length" of a mutation. The discrepancy between the long distance and the sum of the two short distances measures the "length" of the central mutation.

tances. The muton would also be measurable by determining the maximum number of mutations, separable by recombination, that can be packed into a portion of the map.

It must be emphasized that the genetic units proposed by Benzer are completely operational in meaning and origin. They serve the important function of pointing up the complexity of the word "gene" by making a clear distinction between the several operational components of this word, namely, recombination, mutation, and function. Although it is far too early to suggest that the observations made on bacteriophages may be directly applicable to higher organisms, the results at least give a rational basis for the consideration of such phenomena as pseudoallelism. More important, the high density of mapping attained and the indications therefrom of the size of the recon now make it possible to discuss chemical structure and genetics in the same breath. By making assumptions about the chemical length of the genetic strand of DNA in phage (perhaps on the order of 80,000 nucleotide pairs, in a double helix) and the total "genetic" length (perhaps on the order of 800 recombination units), Benzer is able to suggest that a single nucleotide pair might correspond to about 0.01 recombination units. Since this distance is of the same magnitude as that observed between some of the most closely linked loci on the map (about 0.02 units), it is possible that the techniques employed have, indeed, been able to distinguish the genetic effect of a modification in as few as two pairs of nucleotides in a DNA molecule. If, as we may hope, the details of protein structure in an organism are the reflections of the chemical structure of its genetic material, these calculations would suggest that a mutation may be detectable in the phenotype when as little as a single amino acid replacement has occurred. The reader must view these speculations with absolute candor. The hypothesis is under active experimental test, and we must now rely on the protein chemist to help close the gap between genetic speculation and chemical fact.

Before leaving the subject of genetic fine structure, brief mention must be made of another technique for mapping the substructure of genes. This technique, discovered by Zinder and Lederberg[5] in 1952, relies on a phenomenon known as transduction, in which genetic information in bacterial chromosomes is transmitted from cell to cell by bacteriophage particles. Certain bacteria may be inhabited by so-called temperate bacteriophages which exist in a symbiotic arrangement with their host, wherein they only rarely lyse the bacterial cell. When such lysis *does* occur, the liberated phage particles can infect new host cells and, in the process, carry with them some of the genetic peculiarities of the original host. Only a single phenotypic character is generally transduced at a time, as though the phage were carrying with it a single gene. However, there is occasional transfer of more than one genetic marker in a bundle, and such events enable the investigator to determine the closeness of linkage between two or more functional units of heredity.

The explanation might be offered for transduction in general that parts of the "chromosome" of the phage have exchanged with parts of the bacterial chromosome and that, following the establishment of a new symbiosis, this newly acquired information is unloaded on the new host. Many characteristics of *transduction* are highly reminiscent of *transformation*. In both, transfer of genetic information appears to depend on the physical transfer of DNA, either packaged as in phage or free. Both phenomena, although generally involving only a single genetic marker, may occasionally involve several. Transduction has been employed by a number of investigators for the mapping of genetic material in several bacterial species and permits a degree of discrimination comparable to that achieved by Benzer through bacteriophage crossing. However, since the concept of "fine-structure genetics" is quite elegantly illustrated by the bacteriophage approach, we shall defer to the excellent reviews listed below and proceed to the next item of business, the protein molecule.

REFERENCES

1. W. J. Dreyer and G. Koch, *Virology*, **6**, 291 (1958).
2. L. M. Kozloff, M. Lute, and K. Henderson, *J. Biol. Chem.*, **228**, 511 (1957).
3. Discussed by C. Levinthal and C. A. Thomas in *The Chemical Basis of Heredity*. See Suggestions for Further Reading.
4. Summarized in *The Chemical Basis of Heredity*. See Suggestions for Further Reading.
5. N. D. Zinder and J. Lederberg, *J. Bacteriology*, **64**, 679 (1952).

SUGGESTIONS FOR FURTHER READING

The Chemical Basis of Heredity (W. D. McElroy and B. Glass, editors), Johns Hopkins Press, Baltimore, 1957.

Cold Spring Harbor Symposia on Quantitative Biology, **21**, "Genetic Mechanisms: Structure and Function" (1956).

Cold Spring Harbor Symposia on Quantitative Biology, **17**, "Viruses" (1953).

Figure 52. A model of the myoglobin molecule based on X-ray crystallographic data. We can deduce from the dimensions of this model, and from the known number of amino acid residues in myoglobin, that certain portions of the polypeptide chain of myoglobin must be coiled to form an internal secondary structure. The gray disk-like structure shown in the photograph represents the porphyrin prosthetic group, and the light- and dark-colored spheres represent heavy-metal derivatives which were attached to the protein to facilitate analysis of the diffraction data. Dr. J. C. Kendrew of the University of Cambridge kindly furnished this photograph.

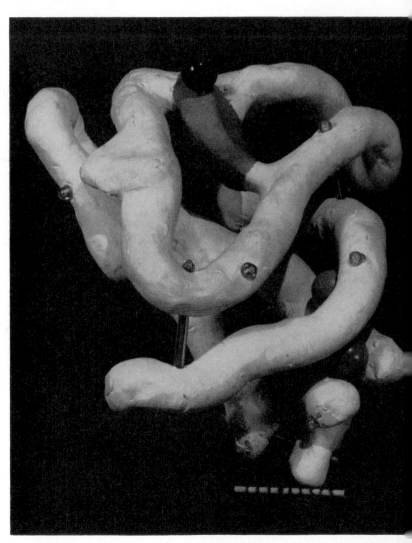

chapter 5

PROTEIN STRUCTURE

The study of the internal structure of proteins in the crystalline form by means of X-ray crystallography indicates a well-defined arrangement of atoms, more or less "frozen" into a definite pattern which is the same for each molecule in the crystal. The crystallographer thus obtains a picture of *the* structure of a protein which is rigid and essentially invariant (Figure 52). From the purely chemical point of view such a picture is completely satisfactory. In living cells, however, proteins are not in the solid state but are dissolved in the intracellular fluid and can be shown to be in a constant state of minor rearrangement in response to shifting hydrogen ion concentrations and salt levels and to reversible adsorption to intracellular surfaces.

In considering such fluctuations it is convenient to think of the chemical fabric of proteins in terms of three distinct categories, christened by K. Linderstrøm-Lang—primary, secondary, and tertiary structure. The term primary structure refers to the fixed amino acid sequence of the polypeptide chain (or chains) making up the backbone of the molecule. This category also includes those covalent bonds that form fixed sites of cross-linkage such as the disulfide bonds between half-cystine residues and the phosphate diester linkages of certain phosphoproteins.

The concept of secondary structure is based, to a large extent, on

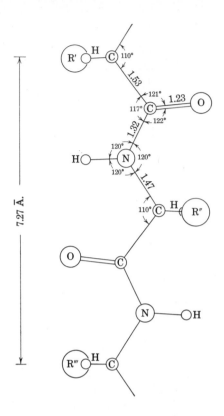

Figure 53. The dimensions of a fully extended polypeptide chain as derived from X-ray crystallographic data. From R. B. Corey and J. Donahue, *J. Am. Chem. Soc.,* **72,** 2899 (1950).

the relatively recent discovery of helical coiling in proteins, stabilized by hydrogen bonds between the amide (CONH) linkages of the chain. A number of helical arrangements of the polypeptide chain may be constructed with atomic models which fit the geometrical restrictions imposed by the bond angles and interatomic distances that have been determined by the X-ray crystallographer on low molecular weight substances such as di- and tripeptides (Figure 53). These various models differ in respect to the number of amino acid residues per turn of helix, in the pitch of the helical screw, and in the amount of unfilled space left within their centers. Of all the helices that have been seriously considered as components of protein structure, the so-called α-helix appears to be the most probable. In this structure the maximum number of intrahelical hydrogen bonds are formed between the CONH linkages, and the structure is consequently a fairly stable one. Perhaps most important, the atoms comprising the peptide bond fall in one plane without strain. The likelihood of such a planar configuration is high as judged from crystal-

THE MOLECULAR BASIS OF EVOLUTION

Dimensions of an α–helix

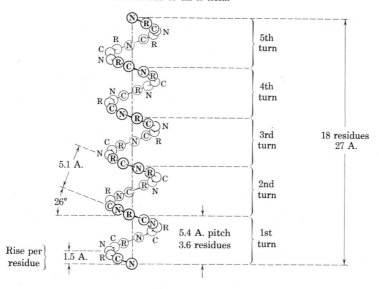

5th turn

4th turn

3rd turn

18 residues
27 A.

2nd turn

5.1 A.

26°

5.4 A. pitch
3.6 residues

1st turn

Rise per residue

1.5 A.

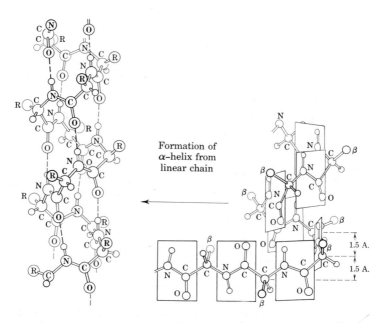

Formation of
α–helix from
linear chain

1.5 A.

1.5 A.

Figure 54. A schematic representation of the process of coiling an extended poly-peptide chain into the α-helical configuration. Redrawn from L. Pauling and R. B. Corey, *Proc. Intern. Wool Textile Research Conf.*, **B**, 249 (1955).

lographic studies of model peptides like that shown in Figure 53. Figure 54 illustrates the way in which the extended, "β-keratin" form of the polypeptide chain is coiled into the α-helical configuration. Each amide group is linked to the third amide group beyond by a hydrogen bond. A complete turn of the helix contains 3.7 amino acid residues, each residue contributing 1.47 A. of linear translation along the central axis. The pitch of the "screw" is thus 5.44 A.

Recent physicochemical studies on proteins and polypeptide model substances have shown that, in spite of the stabilization given by the internal hydrogen bonds, the helical structure is not sufficiently stable to exist in solution but unfolds into a random, disoriented strand. Stabilization of the helical coiling requires the presence of disulfide bridges and/or *tertiary structure,* and it is probable that only those parts of proteins which are properly anchored by such bonds can maintain the helical configuration. Tertiary bonds include such examples as the van der Waals interactions, the agglomeration of lyophobic side chains by mutual repulsion of solvent, and such special hydrogen bonds as might exist between the hydroxyl groups of tyrosine or the ε-amino groups of lysine and electronegative groups elsewhere along the chain (Figure 55). The variations, reversible and irreversible, that are possible in the secondary and tertiary structure of proteins are, basically, functions of the primary,

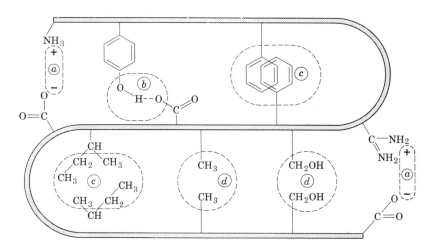

Figure 55. Some types of noncovalent bonds which stabilize protein structure: (*a*) Electrostatic interaction; (*b*) hydrogen bonding between tyrosine residues and carboxylate groups on side chains; (*c*) interaction of nonpolar side chains caused by the mutual repulsion of solvent; (*d*) van der Waals interactions.

covalent structure of the protein, which is fixed and invulnerable to modification by ordinary environmental fluctuations. Thus, a real understanding of the physicochemical behavior of a protein in solution must depend on a detailed knowledge of its structure in the organic chemical sense.

To appreciate our present state of knowledge we must attempt to view the problem from the position occupied by protein chemistry some fifteen years ago. In spite of a large body of rather precise data dealing with the behavior of proteins in solution, there existed a sort of mystical aura around macromolecular structures arising, for the most part, from the almost complete absence of accurate information on amino acid content and arrangement. The necessary background for the modern approach was provided when Fred Sanger and his colleagues[1] undertook the study of the insulin molecule and demonstrated that there existed, in the structural analysis of at least one protein, no insuperable chemical difficulties. The confidence engendered by Sanger's accomplishments and the techniques he employed have led to similar structural attacks on a number of other proteins during the past five years. This accumulated experience has now brought us to a point where we may, with good expectations of success, undertake the elucidation of the structure of nearly any protein whose molecular weight is within reasonable limits. At the present time, for example, complete sequential formulas are available for the insulins and adrenocorticotropic hormones of several species, for bovine glucagon, and for the melanocyte-stimulating hormones of pig and beef pituitary glands. The sequences of several enzymes, including ribonuclease, papain, and lysozyme, should be completed within a relatively short time, and many other biologically active proteins are under study in a number of laboratories.

Although it is outside the scope of this book to discuss, with any degree of completeness, the methodology involved in the determination of the sequence of amino acids in polypeptide chains, some consideration of this subject will be of interest. In the following summary we shall assume the availability of protein samples of proven homogeneity. A specific consideration of the heterogeneity of individual proteins, and of the implications of heterogeneity with regard to protein synthesis and genetics, will be made in subsequent chapters.

For reasons of personal familiarity with the protein, I have chosen as a model substance for the discussion of methodology the enzyme ribonuclease. This enzyme, which has been found in all cells tested so far, catalyzes a transphosphorylation reaction which leads to the

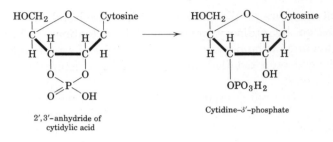

2′,3′-anhydride of
cytidylic acid

Cytidine-3′-phosphate

Figure 56. A synthetic material which is hydrolyzed by ribonuclease.

hydrolysis of certain phosphate diester linkages in ribonucleic acid involving pyrimidine nucleotide residues. The cleavage of a variety of synthetic substrates, of the sort shown in Figure 56, is also catalyzed by the enzyme and forms the basis for a convenient enzymatic assay. Although its specific role in cell metabolism is, as yet, unknown, it seems likely that ribonuclease plays an important part in some aspect of the process of protein biosynthesis (see Chapter 10). Large quantities of ribonuclease are formed and secreted by the pancreas, and the pancreatic enzyme must catalyze extensive hydrolysis of ribonucleic acid in the intestine.

The structure of bovine pancreatic ribonuclease has been under study for several years in two laboratories in which, fortunately for the present illustrative purposes, rather different methods have been employed toward the same end. As the first step in the study of the structure of any protein, it is necessary to obtain an accurate set of analytical data on the amino acid composition of the molecule. Such data were furnished for ribonuclease by Hirs, Moore, and Stein,[2] who established, by careful chromatographic techniques, that the protein contained 124 amino acid residues. Their results may be expressed in terms of the formula:

$$Asp_{15}, Glu_{12}, Gly_3, Ala_{12}, Val_9, Leu_2,$$

$$Ileu_3, Ser_{15}, Thr_{10}, Cys_8, Met_4, Pro_4,$$

$$Phe_3, Tyr_6, His_4, Lys_{10}, Arg_4, (NH_3)_{17}$$

where each amino acid is indicated by an abbreviation derived from the first three letters of its name. Most readers of this book will be familiar with these abbreviated formulas, but for the benefit of those who are not a complete list is given in Table 3.

TABLE 3
Amino Acid Composition of Bovine, Pancreatic Ribonuclease[2]

Amino Acid	Abbreviations[a]	Number Residues per Molecule (mol. wt. 13,683)	Amino Acid	Abbreviations[a]	Number Residues per Molecule (mol. wt. 13,683)
Aspartic acid	(Asp)	15	Methionine	(Met)	4
Glutamic acid	(Glu)	12	Proline	(Pro)	4
Glycine	(Gly)	3	Phenylalanine	(Phe)	3
Alanine	(Ala)	12	Tyrosine	(Tyr)	6
Valine	(Val)	9	Histidine	(His)	4
Leucine	(Leu)	2	Lysine	(Lys)	10
Isoleucine	(Ileu)	3	Arginine	(Arg)	4
Serine	(Ser)	15	Amide NH_3		(17)
Threonine	(Thr)	10			
Half-cystine	(Cys)	8	Total number of residues		124

Not present in ribonuclease are tryptophan (Try) and cysteine (CySH). Cysteic acid ($CySO_3H$) is formed by oxidation of cysteine and cystine, and $MetO_2$ by oxidation of methionine. Amide nitrogens are derived from the side-chain carboxyl groups of glutamic acid and aspartic acid and are generally indicated as $Glu(NH_2)$ and $Asp(NH_2)$, although abbreviated forms, such as Gn and An, seem more convenient.

[a] As suggested by E. Brand and J. T. Edsall, *Ann. Rev. Biochem.*, **16**, 224 (1947).

To determine whether or not the 124 amino acids are arranged in a single, or in multiple, cross-linked polypeptide chains, various chemical and physical studies were carried out as summarized in Figure 57. The presence of as many as five cross-linked chains was possible in ribonuclease since the molecule contained four *cystine* residues. The protein was, therefore, oxidized with performic acid, which converts the sulfur atoms in disulfide bonds into sulfonic acid groups. Ultracentrifugation and viscosity measurements permitted calculations which indicated that the oxidized protein had essentially the same molecular weight as the native protein. The presence of more than one chain would have been reflected in a marked lowering of the average molecular weight as estimated by these physical measurements.

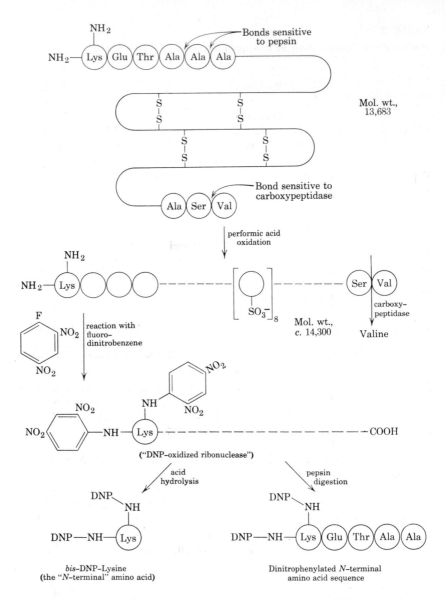

Figure 57. Demonstration of the presence of a single polypeptide chain in bovine pancreatic ribonuclease. The native molecule is oxidized with performic acid to yield an extended polypeptide chain. This derivative contains only a single N-terminal and a single C-terminal end group.

THE MOLECULAR BASIS OF EVOLUTION

The single-chain character of the protein was further indicated by "end group analysis." The only free α-amino groups in proteins are those present on the amino acids at the termini of polypeptide chains. These amino groups may be reacted with reagents such as dinitrofluorobenzene, which forms a dinitrophenyl (DNP) derivative of the protein in which (Figure 57) the N-terminal (i.e., NH_2-terminal) amino acids have been converted to their DNP derivatives. Such a modified protein may be cleaved with acid or with proteolytic enzymes, and the DNP-N-terminal amino acid residue, or peptide, may be isolated and characterized chemically. By this method, evidence was obtained for only a single free α-amino group in the protein, present in the sequence Lys.Glu.Thr.Ala. For partial characterization of the C-terminal (i.e., COOH-terminal) end of the protein, the enzyme carboxypeptidase was used as one of several tools for the specific cleavage of the peptide bond at this end of the chain. This enzyme removed valine from ribonuclease, with only traces of other amino acids. The presence of single N-terminal and C-terminal residues in the protein confirmed the physical evidence for a single chain.

Hydrolysis of the oxidized chain has been carried out by a variety of proteolytic enzyme "reagents," since these tend to catalyze a much more limited number of peptide bond cleavages than do such agents as mineral acids. Indeed, it now appears that nonspecific hydrolysis by acids can, in general, be avoided at this stage and is of particular use only in the subsequent study of the sequence of the smaller peptide subunits produced by preliminary enzymatic attack.

Figure 58 is a schematic outline of two general methods of approach to the detailed structural analysis of polypeptide chains that have been applied to the ribonuclease molecule and are of general applicability. In both techniques the native structure of the protein is unfolded by cleavage of the disulfide bridges, either by oxidative methods to yield cysteic acid residues in place of half-cystine residues, or by reductive cleavage followed by chemical masking of the resulting sulfhydryl group by some suitable agent such as iodoacetic acid. (The latter method for cleavage has an intrinsic advantage over the oxidative method since it can be applied to proteins containing tryptophan, an amino acid residue which is extremely labile to the conditions of disulfide oxidation by performic acid.)

In method A one sample is hydrolyzed by trypsin which cleaves the chain at points following lysine or arginine residues, and another by chymotrypsin (or some other protease with different specificities from trypsin). As indicated, a completely different, but overlapping,

Method A

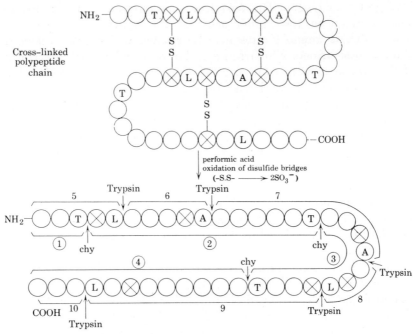

Method B

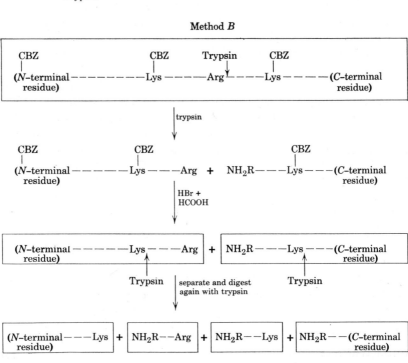

set of peptide fragments is obtained; this set may then be subjected to analysis and arranged in linear order on the basis of overlaps in composition.

In method *B* trypsin cleavage is restricted to positions following arginine only, by masking the ϵ-amino groups of the lysine residues with either dinitrophenyl groups or carbobenzoxy groups. In this method, therefore, we obtain a number of fragments one greater than the number of arginine residues in the protein. All the fragments contain *C*-terminal arginine except the one derived from the *C*-terminus of the chain (which fixes its position). Method *B* depends on the subsequent determination of the sequence of small peptides isolated from random hydrolysates prepared with acid or with some very nonspecific protease such as subtilisin (a bacterial protease) which yields short, easily manageable, peptides. These arginine-containing sequences are then used as connecting links between the larger fragments originally separated from the digest of the carbobenzoxylated protein.

The Rockefeller Institute group, following method *A*, have reacted separate samples of oxidized ribonuclease with trypsin, pepsin, and chymotrypsin. These hydrolysates have then been separated into component peptide fragments by column chromatography. A consideration of overlaps has then enabled these investigators to reconstruct large portions of the peptide chain. As an example of such a reconstruction, let us examine the experimental data which permitted Hirs, Moore, and Stein[3] to arrive at a partial reconstruction of the ribonuclease chain.

A typical analytical pattern is shown in Figure 59*a*, obtained by means of a Dowex-50 ion exchange column through which was passed a tryptic digest of oxidized ribonuclease under proper conditions of elution. The peptide peaks emerging from the column have then been hydrolyzed and rerun separately on subsequent Dowex-50 col-

◀ ───

Figure 58. Two approaches to the determination of the sequential arrangement of amino acids in a polypeptide chain. In method *A* the chain is digested with two or more proteolytic enzymes. The resulting fragments are then separated and analyzed for amino acid composition. A partial reconstruction of the molecule can then be made on the basis of overlapping amino acid compositions. The symbols T, L, and A represent tyrosine, lysine, and arginine respectively. In method *B* the number of cleavages caused by the proteolytic enzyme, trypsin, is limited to those bonds in which the carbonyl of the peptide bond is donated by an arginine residue. To arrange the fragments in their proper order we must first determine the nature of the amino acids in the immediate vicinity of each of the arginine residues.

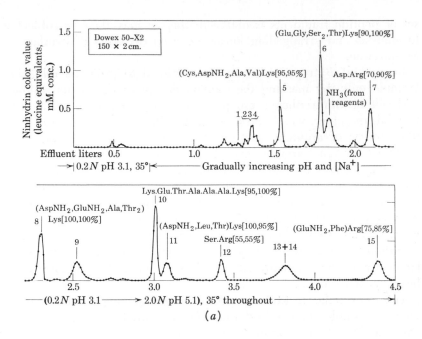

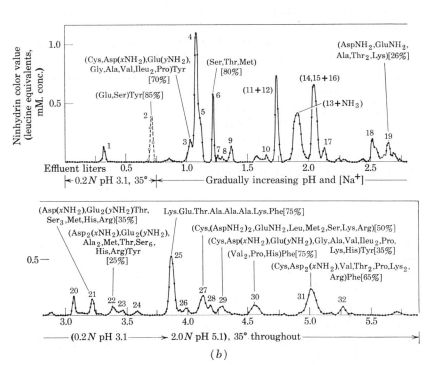

THE MOLECULAR BASIS OF EVOLUTION

umns for amino acid analysis (the results are included in the figure). Similar analysis of a chymotryptic digest of oxidized ribonuclease yielded the results shown in Figure 59b.

The data in Figures 59a and 59b, when considered together with the known N-terminal sequence and with the knowledge that certain residues occur in ribonuclease in only limited numbers (e.g. phenylalanine, 3; glycine, 3; methionine and histidine, 4; etc.) permit the partial reconstruction of the sequence of the enzyme as shown in Figure 60. The parentheses surround the residues that may be grouped together and thus be given approximate linear assignments along the chain. Amide nitrogen atoms, unless specifically attributable to individual aspartic or glutamic acid residues, are distributed in an arbitrary fashion to the dicarboxylic amino acids within any given parenthesis.

The general approach described in Figure 58, method B, yields results that are in accord with the results obtained by method A. Since there exist four arginine residues in ribonuclease, we may expect five peptides of varying size by the application of this method. These peptides were, indeed, shown to be formed by trypsin digestion and, following isolation, were analyzed and partially characterized in terms of terminal sequences. Their composition is given in Table 4. Subsequent characterization of smaller arginine-containing sequences isolated from digests prepared with pepsin or partial acid hydrolysis permitted the alignment of these fragments in the order, A–B–C–D–E. Comparison of the partial reconstructions possible through the use of the two methods indicate how the different sets of information may be fitted together to give a final picture with greater detail than on the basis of either alone.

To construct a final picture of the covalent structure of the protein requires, in addition to the elucidation of the complete sequence of each peptide fragment, a study of the disulfide bridges. The location of these can be determined by application of the methods introduced by Sanger and his colleagues in the case of insulin. The na-

◄───

Figure 59. Separation of the peptides in proteolytic hydrolysates of oxidized ribonuclease. (a) A 20-hour tryptic hydrolysate of a 200-mg. sample of protein, chromatographed on a 150 x 1.8-cm. column of Dowex 50-X2. The points represent the ninhydrin color value given by aliquots of each of the fractions, expressed in leucine equivalents. Figures in brackets represent the yield of each peptide after 3 and 20 hours of trypsin hydrolysis, respectively. From C. H. W. Hirs, S. Moore, and W. H. Stein, *J. Biol. Chem.*, **219**, 623 (1956). (b) Peptides in a chymotryptic hydrolysate of oxidized ribonuclease. From C. H. W. Hirs, W. H. Stein, and S. Moore, *J. Biol. Chem.*, **221**, 151 (1956).

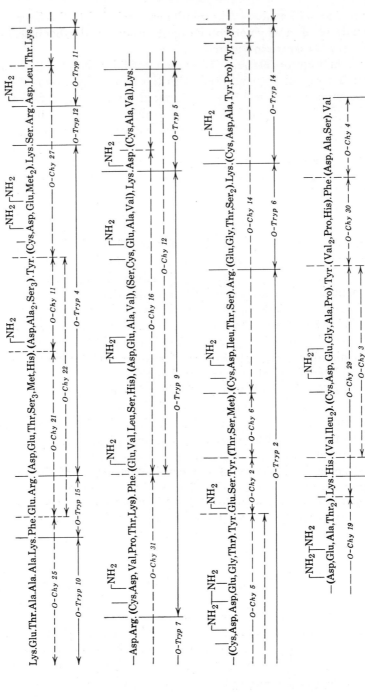

Figure 60. A partial reconstruction of the polypeptide chain of ribonuclease based on procedures such as those described in Figure 58a. From C. H. W. Hirs, W. H. Stein, and S. Moore, *J. Biol. Chem.*, **221**, 151 (1956).

TABLE 4

Partial Structure of the Five Peptides Produced by Application of "Method B" to Oxidized Ribonuclease

Peptide	Structure
A	Lys.Glu.Thr.Ala.Ala.Ala.Lys.Phe.Glu.Arg.

A
↑   ↑ ↑   ↑ ↑   ↑
A   P P   T P   T

B   Glu.(Thr,Ser$_6$,Asp$_3$,His.Met$_3$,Ala$_2$,Tyr,Cys,Glu).Lys.Ser.Arg.
    ↑   ↑
    T   T

C   Asp.Leu.Thr.Lys.Asp.Arg.
   ↑   ↑   ↑
   A   T   T

D   CySO$_3$.(Lys$_3$,Pro,Val$_5$,Asp$_5$,Thr$_3$,Phe,His,Glu$_5$,Ser$_4$,Leu,Ala$_3$,
    Cys$_3$,Gly,Tyr$_2$,Met).Ser.Ileu.Thr.(Asp,Cys).Arg.
    ↑   ↑   ↑
    C   A   T

E   Glu.(Ser$_2$,Thr$_3$,Gly$_2$,Lys$_3$,Tyr$_3$,Pro$_3$,Asp$_3$,Ala$_3$,Cys$_2$,Glu$_2$,
    His$_2$,Ileu$_2$,Val$_3$).Phe.Asp.Ala.Ser.Val
    ↑   ↑
    P   A

After digestion of carbobenzoxylated, oxidized ribonuclease with trypsin, the digest was decarbobenzoxylated by treatment with anhydrous HBr in glacial acetic acid. The five peptides were then separated by combined paper electrophoresis and paper chromatography and each one hydrolyzed further with acid (A), pepsin (P), trypsin (T), or chymotrypsin (C). A study of the composition of the fragments produced by these latter digestions permitted a partial reconstruction of the sequence as shown above.

tive protein, in which these bridges are intact, is digested with various proteases (e.g. trypsin plus chymotrypsin or subtilisin). From such digests can be isolated peptides of *cystine*, carved out from the structure of the cross-linked native molecule. The general approach to the determination of disulfide bridges which has been employed by both the group at the Rockefeller Institute and at the National Heart Institute is given in a disarmingly simplified form in Figure 61.

Following these general procedures, Spackman, Moore, and Stein[3] were able to isolate, for example, a *cystine*-containing peptide which,

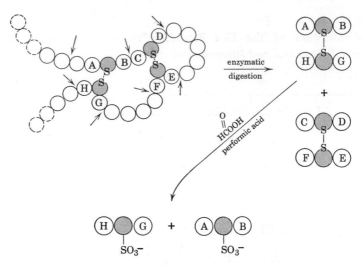

Figure 61. Steps in the determination of how half-cystine residues are paired in disulfide linkage. The cysteic acid-containing peptides derived from each cystine peptide are separated by chromatography and/or electrophoresis. A consideration of their amino acid compositions in terms of the amino acid sequence of the protein will generally permit the location of each half-cystine residue along the polypeptide chain.

upon oxidation with performic acid, yielded the two *cysteic acid*-containing peptides

$$(CySO_3^-, An, Gn, Met_2, Lys) \text{ and}$$
$$(CySO_3^-, An, Ileu, Thr, Ser, Arg)r$$

The amino acid compositions of these peptides are such that the cysteic acid residues could only have been derived from half-cystines 1 and 6 respectively, establishing the presence of a disulfide bridge between these half-cystines in the native protein. (The half-cystines are numbered sequentially from the *N*-terminal end of the chain). In a similar fashion, evidence was obtained for a disulfide bond between half-cystines 4 and 5, and, with some reservations because of the possibility of chemical rearrangements during isolation, between 3 and 7, and 2 and 8. The results of the combined degradative studies of ribonuclease, together with the isolation and tentative characterization of the cystine bridges, permit us to construct a provisional formula for the enzyme as shown in Figure 62. The formula includes much of the total sequence within the parentheses in the reconstructions summarized in Figure 60 and Table 4.

One additional example of the determination of amino acid sequence is summarized in Figure 63. This figure shows, in a nutshell, the general approach used by Li and his colleagues in the study of the structure of the anterior pituitary hormone, adrenocorticotropin (ACTH).[4] The various fragments (see also Chapter 6), some of which were subjected to complete or partial sequence analysis by methods described in some of the references at the end of this chapter, are all consistent with only one unique sequence as shown.

Figure 62. The structure of bovine pancreatic ribonuclease. This figure has been constructed from the combined studies of a number of individuals at the Rockefeller Institute (including Drs. C. H. W. Hirs, S. Moore, S. H. Stein, D. Spackman, and L. Bailey) and at the National Heart Institute (including R. Redfield, J. Cooke, A. Ryle, and C. B. Anfinsen). The positions of the four disulfide bridges are probably as shown, although there is still some question about the bridge between half-cystine residues 2 and 8 and that between half-cystine residues 3 and 7, because of the poor yields obtained during the isolation of cystine peptides and because of the possibility of chemical rearrangements which might have occurred during certain steps in the sequence analysis of these peptides. At the present time some 95 residues may be assigned with reasonable certainty to definite positions in the polypeptide chain, which contains 124 residues in all. The residues that are shaded may be assigned to the general region of the molecule indicated, but their exact position in the sequence must await further double-checking by stepwise degradation.

Amino Acid Sequence

Hydrolytic Agent	
Trypsin	Ser.Tyr.Ser(Met.Glu.His.Phe)Arg
Chymotrypsin	Arg.Try( )
Trypsin	Try.Gly.Lys.Pro.Val.Gly.Lys
Trypsin	Lys.Arg
Trypsin	Lys.Arg.Arg
Trypsin	Arg.Pro.Val.Lys
Acid	Pro(Val,Lys,Val,Tyr)
Trypsin	Val.Tyr.Pro.Ala.Gly.Glu(Asp,Asp,Glu,Ala,Ser,Glu,Ala,Phe,Pro,Leu,Glu,Phe)
Acid	Ala(Gly,Glu,Asp)
Pepsin	Asp.Glu
Pepsin	Asp(Glu,Ala)
Pepsin	Asp(Glu,Ala)Ser
Pepsin	Glu(Ala,Ser)
Pepsin	Ser.Glu
Pepsin	Ser(Glu,Ala)
Pepsin	Ser(Glu,Ala,Phe)
Pepsin	Glu.Ala.Phe
Pepsin	Phe(Pro,Leu,Glu)
Pepsin	Pro(Leu,Glu,Phe)

Complete sequence: Ser.Tyr.Ser.Met.Glu.His.Phe.Arg.Try.Gly.Lys.Pro.Val.Gly.Lys.Lys.Arg.Arg.Pro.Val.Lys.Val.Tyr.Pro.Ala.Gly.Glu.Asp.Asp.Glu.Ala.Ser.Glu.Ala.
1 2 3 4 5 6 7 8 9 10 11 12 13 14 15 16 17 18 19 20 21 22 23 24 25 26 27 28 29 30 31 32 33 34
Phe.Pro.Leu.Glu.Phe
35 36 37 38 39

Figure 63. A reconstruction of the structure of α-corticotropin from the structure of the peptides attained by proteolytic and partial acid hydrolysis.[1]

As we shall discuss subsequently, the knowledge of the complete covalent structure of a protein molecule is, unfortunately, not a magic key to the understanding of physicochemical and catalytic behavior in itself. A real appreciation of Nature's intent with respect to protein molecules must be sought through additional considerations of structure in three-dimensional terms.

Secondary and Tertiary Structure

Having established the details of the covalent structure of a protein, we may proceed to a comparison of these organochemical details with physicochemical behavior in solution. The total number of charges, positive and negative, along the polypeptide chains should agree with the values determined by titrating the protein with acid or base. A knowledge of the number of tyrosine, phenylalanine, and tryptophan residues in the molecule should make it possible to estimate, in advance, the shape and height of ultraviolet light absorption curves in the wavelengths from 250 to 290 mμ. Determinations of the content of sulfhydryl groups in the protein should confirm the analytical values for cysteine.

It was not surprising to the physical biochemists at work on such comparisons to find that these predictions seldom coincide with actuality. In general, many charges are masked or sequestered, absorption spectra are shifted from the theoretical, and sulfhydryl groups often appear in force only after serious denaturation of the protein molecule. The deviations are attributable to a number of known, and probably many unknown, parameters of secondary and tertiary structure which we shall attempt briefly to summarize.

We have already referred to the likelihood of helical coiling in proteins as the central theme of secondary structure. According to the dimensions of the α-helix and to the pitch of its screw, each residue in the polypeptide chain should contribute 1.5 A. to the length of the helical coil. Thus, in a helix with n residues, the total length of the coil should be $n \times 1.5$ A. (see Figure 54). By an extensive series of studies of the viscosity, light scattering, and sedimentation properties of the synthetic polyamino acid poly-γ-benzyl-L-glutamate in favorable solvents, Doty and his colleagues obtained data in full agreement with this theoretical calculation; that is, experimentally determined molecular lengths, in angstroms, were equal to the number of residues in the chain multiplied by 1.5.[5] It should be emphasized in the following that, although the word "helix" is used freely for convenience, the presence of α-helical coiling in globular proteins is supported only by very circumstantial evidence. We may safely assume that there exists *some* sort of ordered folding within such proteins, but we must be wary of getting into the habit of thinking in terms of the α-helix exclusively until more data become available. It has not been established that all *proteins* contain such a structure, and the examination of this point, with special reference to globular proteins, is a particularly active area of research at the present time.

The study of the properties of helical systems in solution depends to a large degree on the use of optical rotatory methods. The mathematical theory of optical rotation by proteins is extremely complex and speculative. In spite of theoretical difficulties, however, there appears to be a high degree of consistency and predictability in connection with optical rotatory measurements, and we can gain an adequate appreciation of the usefulness of the method from a purely empirical point of view.

The optical rotation of a protein is made up of several components, one of which is the average rotation of the individual residues in the polypeptide chains. Superimposed on this rotation is the contribution of the ordered, repeating character of the helical configuration when this is present in the structure. It has been found experimentally, by studying the rotation of synthetic polyamino acids which can be made to assume varying degrees of helical coiling by modification of the solvent, that fully coiled chains possess an optical rotation approximately 90° (for the D line of the sodium lamp) greater than that to be expected as an average for the residues themselves. This completely empirical number may be used as a basis for calculating the content of helical coiling in a protein, according to the following equation:

$$\% \text{ helical coiling} = \frac{R_{\text{folded}} - R_{\text{unfolded}}}{90°} \times 100$$

The mean residue rotation of the folded protein, R_{folded}, is obtained by measurements on the native protein in water, and R_{unfolded} is estimated by measuring in the presence of such materials as urea or guanidine, or at elevated temperatures, under which conditions coiling, stabilized by hydrogen bonds, may be assumed to be destroyed. Some examples of optical rotatory measurements are given in Table 5 together with estimates of the amounts of helical coiling in these proteins. A measure of the rotation of the unfolded state may also be obtained on samples in which disulfide cross-linkages have been

TABLE 5

Rotatory Properties of Native Proteins in the Folded and Unfolded States[a]

Protein	R_{folded}	8 M urea $R_{unfolded}$	Calculated Per Cent of Protein in Helix
Ribonuclease	−90.7	−126.5	40
Insulin	−36.5	− 98.3	68
Ovalbumin	−33.9	−106.8	81
Lysozyme	−53.3	− 96.0	47
Chymotrypsin	−71.9	−115.9	49
Silk fibroin[b]	−40.	− 51.3	12

[a] C. Schellman and J. A. Schellman, *Compt. rend. trav. lab. Carlsberg, Ser. chim.*, **30**, 463–500 (1958).

[b] Silk fibroin is an example of a protein which is almost free of stabilizing cross-linkages and consequently exists in a form nearly free of secondary structure. Its mean residue optical rotation in urea ($R_{unfolded}$) is low owing to the high content of the optically inactive amino acid glycine.

broken by reductive or oxidative cleavage. In the absence of such stabilizing linkages, the helix is apparently unstable, and we observe rotations such as might be expected for the average amino acid residue, that is, about −100 to −120°. Disulfide bridges are not enough in themselves, however, to insure helical configuration in a protein molecule. We must take into account the fact that agents like urea can cause disorientation of secondary structure, even in the presence of intact disulfide linkages. It seems certain that a number of tertiary structural features also contribute to the determination of protein structure in solution. The presence of such structural interactions are indicated by the lack of agreement, mentioned earlier, between the experimentally determined values for ionizable groups, sulfhydryl groups, and the like and the values predicted from sequence data alone.

Functional groups which exhibit modified properties can be studied in a quantitative way. An excellent example comes from the spectrophotometric examination of proteins. It was first observed by Crammer and Neuberger[6] in 1943 that the spectrum of ovalbumin in the region attributable to tyrosine residue absorption was shifted to shorter wavelengths as compared with the spectrum of tyrosine itself. These results indicated that the absorption of light energy by the tyrosine chromophore had been modified in some way by the environ-

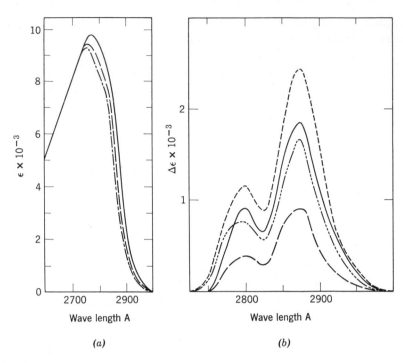

Figure 64. (a) Spectra of inactive ribonuclease (top curve), of inactive derivative of ribonuclease isolated from limited pepsin digests (middle curve), and of an exhaustive pepsin digest of ribonuclease (bottom curve). (b) Differences in extinction at various wavelengths between native ribonuclease and a complete pepsin digest of ribonuclease (upper curve), of the inactive pepsin derivative (second curve), of ribonuclease in 8 M urea (third curve), and of ribonuclease in 8 M urea in the presence of 0.003 M phosphate ions (bottom curve). From C. B. Anfinsen, *Federation Proc.*, **16,** 783 (1957).

ment of the tyrosine residues within the structure of the protein molecule. Similar observations were subsequently made for a number of other proteins including ribonuclease, lysozyme, and serum albumin. It was ultimately shown that the shift, characteristic of the abnormal spectrum (shown for ribonuclease in Figure 64), could be abolished by agents like urea which cause the rupture of hydrogen bonds. Simultaneously there were released, in a titratable form, carboxyl groups which had hitherto been masked and unavailable to titration by alkali. The number of such unmasked acid groups approximated the number of tyrosine residues which, it could be calculated, were responsible for the shift in extinction maximum. These findings furnished evidence for the presence of tyrosine hydroxyl-carboxylate interactions of the type we have already shown schematically in Figure 55.* The stage was, of course, set for the detection of these particular hydrogen-bonded interactions since there is available here a simple method of observation, namely the spectrophotometer. Other hydrogen-bonded combinations, for example, between amino groups and carboxyl groups or between two carboxyl groups, may also be expected to exist in proteins, but they have so far escaped detection because of the lack of an adequate assay procedure for them.

Our consideration of the protein structure up to this point has been concerned with *static or equilibrium* properties. The covalent bonds in proteins can be relied on to resist most of the environmental fluctuations to which proteins are normally exposed. In a sense, they determine the three-dimensional potentialities by establishing a fixed distribution of charges and lyophobic groupings along the polypeptide chain and by acting as the basis for rigid and permanent cross-linkages. The covalent bonds do, however, have a certain degree of flexibility, and the slight deformations in bond angles between atoms, together with the rotation of atoms around single bonds, make it possible for a protein to assume a vast number of slightly different configurations in solution. When we measure the viscosity, optical rotation, or ultracentrifugal behavior of a protein preparation, the results obtained relate only to the *average* molecule in the solution. In general, the deviation from this average is probably fairly small because some arrangements have a much higher stability (i.e., a lower total free energy of configuration). The small fluctuations in configuration which do occur are, however, undoubtedly of considerable importance in connection with the biological activity of proteins and fortunately can be studied by means of a few specialized techniques which measure the *dynamic* aspects of protein structure.

As we have discussed earlier, it is possible to estimate the extent of helical coiling in proteins by measuring optical rotatory properties if we are willing to equate "repeating units of asymmetry" with "helix." The theoretical and experimental support for this assump-

* It will be noted that the spectral characteristics of tyrosine in native ribonuclease (and in other proteins in which similar effects have been observed) resemble to some extent those exhibited on ionization of the phenolic hydroxyl group of free tyrosine. In both instances a shift of the spectrum toward longer wavelengths as well as an increase in absorption occurs. It seems likely that formation of a hydrogen bond could bring about spectral changes analogous to those of ionization by increasing the phenolic O—H bond distance. Indeed a number of spectrophotometric studies on substituted phenols have demonstrated a shift of the spectrum toward the red under conditions favoring hydrogen bond formation.

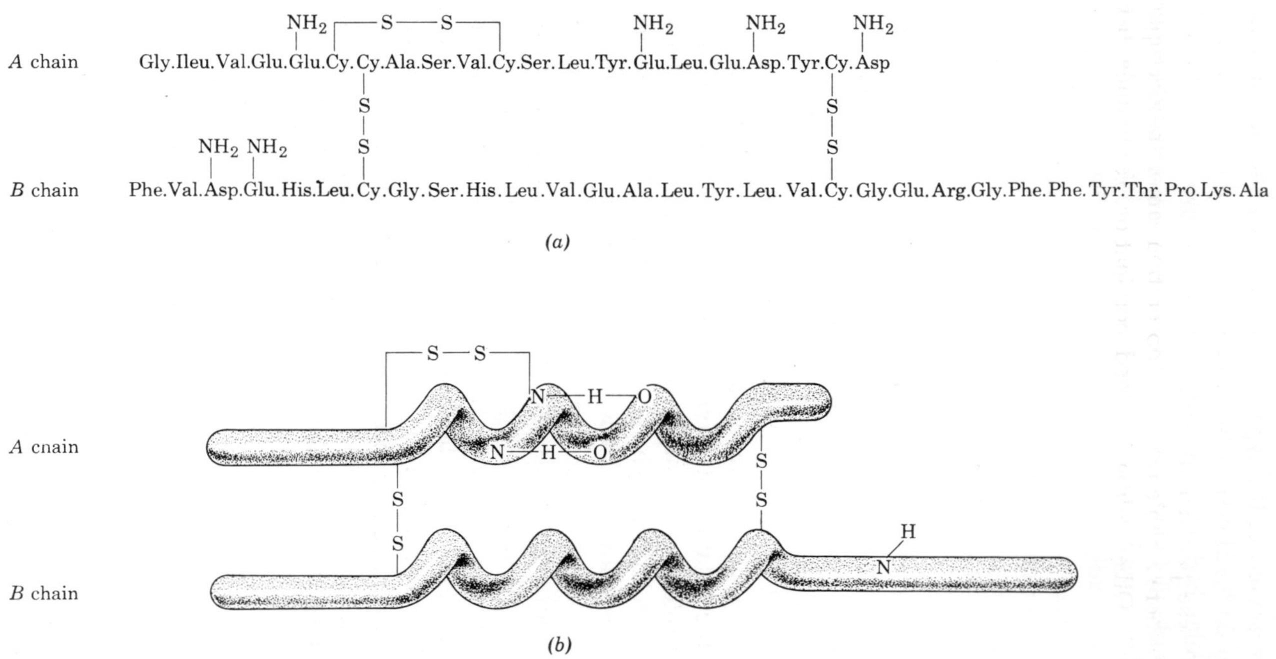

A chain

NH_2 —— S —— S

NH_2 NH_2 NH_2 NH_2

Gly.Ileu.Val.Glu.Glu.Cy.Cy.Ala.Ser.Val.Cy.Ser.Leu.Tyr.Glu.Leu.Glu.Asp.Tyr.Cy.Asp

     S —— S   S —— S

NH_2 NH_2

B chain

Phe.Val.Asp.Glu.His.Leu.Cy.Gly.Ser.His.Leu.Val.Glu.Ala.Leu.Tyr.Leu.Val.Cy.Gly.Glu.Arg.Gly.Phe.Phe.Tyr.Thr.Pro.Lys.Ala

(a)

A chain

B chain

(b)

Figure 65. The structure of insulin (from A. P. Ryle, F. Sanger, L. F. Smith, and R. Kitai, *Biochem. J.*, **60**, 541 (1955), and (b) a schematic drawing of how insulin might be coiled within the portion of the molecule which is stabilized by disulfide bridges. Hydrogen atoms involved in bonding between amide groups within this region might be expected to be in much slower equilibrium with the hydrogen atoms of water molecules than those in the free "tails."

tion is good enough to satisfy most experts as a working hypothesis. By assuming, then, the presence of a certain amount of helical coiling in a protein like insulin, various models may be constructed based on the covalent structure derived by Sanger and his colleagues. In constructing such models it is necessary to guess where the helical portion belongs. Guessing is made somewhat easier by the observation that random polypeptide chains without internal cross-linkages do not spontaneously coil up into organized structures, as judged from viscosity studies and from the effect on optical rotatory properties when disulfide cross-linkages are ruptured by oxidation or reduction. Thus, in the case of insulin, whose structure is shown in Figure 65a, we may assume that the 60 per cent or so of the polypeptide chain which appears, polarimetrically, to be in the α-helix form is most likely to be located within the sterically stabilized region between the disulfide bridges joining the A chain to the B chain. The schematic drawing (Figure 65b) is intended to convey the idea of steric hindrance within the coiled portions of the chains. Within such a region of a protein molecule, we might expect to find that the CONH hydrogens involved in the hydrogen bonding of the helix are much less likely to exchange with the hydrogens of the water in which the protein is dissolved than are the hydrogens of side-chain groups or of CONH bonds outside the helical region. It is precisely this relative stability which the technique of *deuterium exchange* can measure, and this technique constitutes one of the most sensitive methods for the measurement of the *dynamic* state of protein structure.[7] Its particular value lies in the fact that, even when other physical measurements indicate that the average, equilibrium form of a protein contains some helical structure, it can measure the degree of deviation from the average resulting from the reversible opening and closing of hydrogen bonds with accordion-like flapping of the helix.

In practice, a protein is "loaded" with deuterium by solution in deuterium oxide for a time sufficient to allow all exchangeable hydrogens to come into equilibrium with the deuterium of the solvent. The protein is then carefully dried. Upon resolution in ordinary water, deuterium atoms equilibrate with the water, and the rate of appearance of deuterium, as measured by density change in the solvent, permits the division of total exchangeable atoms into those that are instantaneously, rapidly, and slowly exchangeable.

In insulin there are 91 theoretically exchangeable hydrogen atoms. These include the hydrogen atoms on the side chains of various amino acid residues and the CONH hydrogens forming the polypeptide

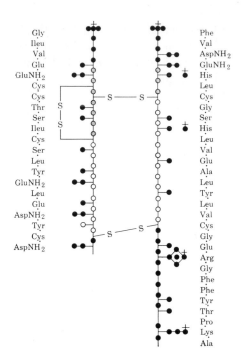

Figure 66. The relative degrees of "exchangeability" of various hydrogen atoms in insulin with deuterium atoms in the solvent: solid circles, instantaneous exchange; crosshatched circles, exchange at intermediate rates; open circles, restricted exchange. From K. Linderstrøm-Lang, *Symposium on Peptide Chemistry*, Special Publications 2, The Chemical Society, London, 1955.

chain. When deuterium-loaded insulin is dissolved in water at 0°C., 60 of these 91 exchange *instantaneously*. With further incubation additional exchange of other hydrogen atoms occurs, but at this temperature the rate of equilibration is relatively slow. In the presence of denaturing agents like urea, or at higher temperatures, the rate of equilibration is greatly increased, and all 91 of the deuterium atoms are ultimately exchanged.

These results have been interpreted by Linderstrøm-Lang[7] as shown in Figure 66. The *slowly* exchangeable hydrogen atoms (indicated by open circles) have been assigned to the region of insulin where the helical configuration is assumed to reside. The assignment of *"rapidly"* exchangeable atoms is somewhat more arbitrary, but can be made, in part, to that region of the A chain within the disulfide "loop" which, when forced into a helical arrangement in models, permits the formation of the intrachain disulfide bridge only with considerable bond deformation.

This interesting method furnishes perhaps the most clear-cut evidence for the existence of a continual flux of local minor rearrangement within the structure of proteins in solution. It brings out, in a particularly dramatic way, the intrinsic instability of the three-dimensional fabric of proteins which can lead to denaturation and loss of biological activity, and it emphasizes some of those structural components whose presence was not even suspected only a few years ago.

REFERENCES

1. F. Sanger in *Currents in Biochemical Research* (D. E. Green, editor), Interscience Publishers, New York, p. 434, 1956.
2. C. H. W. Hirs, W. G. Stein, and S. Moore, *J. Biol. Chem.*, **211**, 941 (1954).
3. S. Moore and W. H. Stein in *The Harvey Lectures 1956–1957*, Academic Press, New York, p. 119, 1958.
4. C. H. Li, I. Geschwind, R. D. Cole, I. Raacke, J. Harris, and J. Dixon, *Nature*, **176**, 687 (1955).
5. B. W. Low in *The Proteins*, volume 1, Part A (H. Neurath and K. Bailey, editors), Academic Press, New York, Chapter 4, 1957.
6. J. L. Crammer, and A. Neuberger, *Biochem. J.*, **37**, 302 (1943).
7. K. V. Linderstrøm-Lang in *Symposium on Peptide Chemistry*, Special Publication 2, The Chemical Society, London, 1955.

SUGGESTIONS FOR FURTHER READING

Anfinsen, C. B., and R. R. Redfield, in *Advances in Protein Chemistry*, volume 11, Academic Press, New York, 1956.
Crick, F. H. C., and J. C. Kendrew, in *Advances in Protein Chemistry*, volume 12, Academic Press, New York, 1957.
Edsall, J. T., and J. Wyman, *Biophysical Chemistry*, volume 1, Academic Press, New York, 1958.
Linderstrøm-Lang, K. V., *Lane Medical Lectures*, volume 6, Stanford University Press, Stanford, 1952.
Low, B. W. and J. T. Edsall in *Currents in Biochemical Research*, (D. E. Green, editor), Interscience Publishers, New York, p. 379, 1956.
Pauling, L., and R. B. Corey, *Proc. Natl. Acad. Sci. U.S.*, **37**, 235 (1951).
Pauling, L., R. B. Corey, and H. R. Branson, *Proc. Natl. Acad. Sci. U.S.*, **37**, 205 (1951).

chapter **6**

THE BIOLOGICAL ACTIVITY
OF PROTEINS
IN RELATION TO STRUCTURE

Wₑ may almost define the life sciences as those
concerned with the elucidation of the mechanisms by which molecules
exert their specific actions on living cells.   In the case of many simple
inorganic ions and organic molecules it has been possible to arrive
at an approximate understanding of their mechanism of action.   We
have some understanding, for example, of the physiological sequelae
of raising or lowering the tonicity of body fluids by the administration
or withdrawal of sodium chloride.   Similarly, the aberrations in the
synaptic transmission of nerve impulses following the administration
of physostigmine may be partially explained by the action of this
drug on the enzyme acetylcholinesterase.   It is a tribute to cellular
complexity that even such well-studied systems as these continue to
be frontiers of research and speculation among those individuals who
are fully conversant with them.

Protein chemists naturally feel that the most likely approach to the understanding of cellular behavior lies in the study of structure and function of protein molecules. This is, perhaps, not an entirely unreasonable point of view. Except for those rare phenomena in biology which are purely physical, the "aliveness" of cells is basically the summation of enzymic catalysis and its regulation.

The field of protein chemistry has now reached a stage of relative sophistication allowing us to think of proteins as organic chemicals rather than as conglomerates of amino acids. In spite of their enormous complexity we now can measure the extent of such phenomena as "denaturation" in terms of rather well-defined changes in specific types of chemical bonds, some of which have been discussed in Chapter 5. Because of this happy situation, we may approach, in a rational way, the relation of specific aspects of covalent and noncovalent protein chemistry to biological activity. Proteins, as *molecules*, must be thought of as consisting of one or more polypeptide chains, cross-linked and coiled through a variety of chemical bonds of varying strengths. Modifications of any of these lead to an entity which is not identical to the original native molecule and which, in a purist sense, may be considered "denatured." From the standpoint of function, however, we may take a somewhat narrower view. The nativeness of an enzyme, *as estimated by its ability to catalyze a reaction*, need not involve the whole of its structure.

Studies of the effect of specific degradation on biologically active proteins are fairly recent. It was observed, however, more than twenty years ago, that various reactive groupings on proteins could be modified by substitution, or conversion to other forms, without loss of function. Perhaps the best-known example of such work is the series of investigations by Herriott and Northrop of the activity of pepsin during progressive acetylation.[1] Pepsin was treated with ketene which converted free amino groups and tyrosine hydroxyl groups to their acetyl derivatives. By this method Herriott was able to prepare a crystalline derivative which contained seven acetyl groups per mole of pepsin and had approximately 60 per cent of the enzyme activity of the original pepsin. He demonstrated that the ultraviolet absorption spectrum of this 60 per cent active material was modified to the extent to be expected for the masking of three tyrosine hydroxyl groups. Further, by cautious hydrolysis at pH 0.0 or at pH 10.0, three acetyl groups could be removed with a simultaneous increase in enzyme activity. These, and other, studies indicated that tyrosine residues were somehow involved in activity and also that acetylation of a number of the free amino groups in the protein *had no effect on function*.

Experiments of this sort have now become relatively commonplace, and there is no doubt that the structures of a large number of enzymes and hormones may be tampered with without inactivation. In spite of such information, the concept persisted, until very recently, that the structure of biologically active proteins was more or less "inviolable" and that the complete and integrated three-dimensional architecture of these proteins was required for function. This concept was nurtured by several theoretical considerations in which the protein molecule was pictured as a network of resonating pathways through which electrons might surge and redistribute during the process of catalysis. The observations of immunology added further support to this concept, since it was well known that relatively minor changes in, for example, the structure of a hapten could lead to a profound modification in the effectiveness of reaction with a specific antibody.

The idea of the "inviolability" of protein structure is now slowly being replaced with the idea of the "functional adequacy of less than the whole." Shortly after Sanger and his colleagues had completed their monumental studies on beef insulin, it was shown by Lens[2] that a known, degradative change in the hormone, namely, the removal of the C-terminal alanine residue of the B chain, did not lead to loss of biological activity. (The evolutionary implications of this observation were not particularly obvious at the time since the experiment was the first of its kind and had to be thought of as an isolated example. Now, however, as the result of many similar observations, we must concern ourselves (see Chapter 11) with the question of why the C-terminal alanine residue is preserved in insulin as a constant structural feature if it serves no function in the biological activity of the hormone.)

Insulin has been subjected to other, more extensive, studies of this sort. However, for the purpose of illustration of the extent to which proteins may be degraded without inactivation, we shall consider instead three other examples about which we have somewhat more information: the pituitary hormone, ACTH, the pancreatic enzyme, ribonuclease, and the plant enzyme, papain. In the following discussion of these examples, two quite different approaches to the structural basis of biological activity will be considered more or less simultaneously. One aim is to show that active polypeptides can be degraded without loss of function, and is concerned mainly with indicating the magnitude of *unessential* parts of structure. The other is directed deliberately toward the delineation of the *essential* parts, that is, the active centers.

Adrenocorticotropic Hormone

Complete sequences have been elucidated for adrenocorticotropic hormone (ACTH) isolated from three species, hog, beef, and sheep. The problem of species variation will be discussed elsewhere. For our present purposes we shall consider only the material isolated from hog pituitaries since the relation between structure and function appears to be the same for the hormones of all three species. Adrenocorticotropic hormone is one of a large number of polypeptides which can be demonstrated in extracts of the anterior pituitary gland. The hormone has been prepared in highly purified form and has been shown to cause the selective stimulation of the adrenal cortex with the release of adrenal steroid hormones. It also causes depletion of the ascorbic acid and cholesterol stores of the adrenal gland and is capable of stimulating the repair of histological changes owing to hypophysectomy.

The sequence of pig ACTH is shown in Figure 67. The polypeptide is composed of 39 amino acid residues and contains several intriguing groups of amino acids, notably the sequence of three hydroxyamino acids, Ser.Tyr.Ser, at the N-terminus and the highly basic grouping, Lys.Lys.Arg.Arg, in positions 15 to 18. The action of carboxypeptidase removes three residues from the C-terminal end of the chain without loss in hormonal activity. A more severe degradation results during limited pepsin digestion with the removal of the eleven C-terminal amino acids, still without change in activity. These experiments establish that, as a maximum, only the first 28 residues of ACTH are required for hormonal function. Paul Bell and his co-workers have recently reduced this estimate, reporting that by mild acid hydrolysis of the chain the last 15 residues may be removed without inactivation.[3]

It has also been possible to characterize the activity of ACTH in terms of specific aspects of structure which *are* essential. Thus it has been found that degradation of the N-terminal end of the chain with leucine aminopeptidase results in complete loss of activity after only one or two residues have been removed. Recent studies on the action of fibrinolysin by White and Gross[4] have further underlined the importance of the first half of the hormone. As is shown in Figure 67, this proteolytic enzyme cleaves the chain at two points, following residues 8 and 15, with complete inactivation.

These various degradative studies establish that at least 16, and perhaps as many as 24, of the amino acids of ACTH are essential ones. The ultimate elucidation of the exact structural requirements

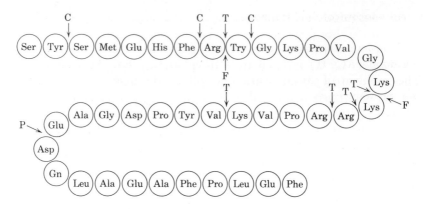

Figure 67. The structure of porcine α-corticotropin. Points of attack by chymotrypsin (C), trypsin (T), pepsin (P), and fibrinolysin (F) are indicated by the arrows.

for ACTH activity must probably await the step-by-step synthesis of the sequence, and such studies are in progress in Klaus Hofmann's laboratory,[5] where the unequivocal synthesis of a peptide corresponding to at least the first 14 amino acids in the polypeptide has been achieved. At last report, the synthetic material had not yet reached sufficient length to exhibit hormonal activity. In the meantime, Boissonnas and his colleagues[6] have reported the synthesis of a biologically active peptide consisting of the first 20 N-terminal amino acids of ACTH. Although the synthesis is not entirely unequivocal, the results give strong support to the conclusions drawn from the degradative work.

The studies on ACTH are of particular interest since they have to do with a substance which is assayed by *in vivo* methods. Investigations of the changes in activity during the degradation of enzymes must generally be controlled by *in vitro* tests. The possibility that functional adequacy in the test tube does not give a true picture of activity in an organized cellular environment adds an aspect of uncertainty to the interpretations. Discounting the rather slim possibility that degraded ACTH is reconverted to native ACTH during activity assays, we have, for this hormone, clear-cut evidence for the "functional adequacy of less than the whole."

Papain

Papain is a powerful proteolytic enzyme present in papaya latex which has been crystallized, both as the native protein and as the mercuri-derivative, by Emil Smith and his colleagues.[7] The enzyme is of considerable interest as a model for the study of the relationships between structure and function because it appears to contain a great deal of structure which is "superfluous" for activity. The molecule contains six sulfhydryl groups, five of which are not reactive with the usual sulfhydryl reagents in the native protein but appear from within the inner regions of the structure only after suitable denaturation. The single reactive sulfhydryl is essential for activity, and complete inactivation occurs when two molecules of the protein react with a single molecule of mercuric ion to form the dimer mercaptide. No other sulfur is present beyond the six cysteine residues, and cross-linkage of the 180 amino acid residue chain through cystine bridges is therefore excluded.

The most exciting development in the studies on papain has been the observation by Hill and Smith[8] that approximately 80 residues may be removed from the N-terminal end of the chain by leucine aminopeptidase without loss in catalytic activity. The remaining C-terminal stretch of amino acids is relatively poor in basic amino acids but rich in tyrosine and valine. The noncritical nature of lysine side chains is indicated by the fact that the ε-amino groups may be converted to the guanido derivatives, by treatment with O-methylisourea, without activation.

Papain is reversibly inactivated by strong urea solutions and, to some extent, irreversibly by guanidinium ions. Under such conditions of denaturation the shape of the molecule is considerably altered as evidenced by changes in the optical rotatory, viscosity, and ultracentrifugal properties. Therefore, although only a portion of the papain chain is essential for catalysis and is apparently not dependent on covalent cross-linkages, there are obviously important secondary and tertiary structural features involved in the determination of its catalytically active center.

Ribonuclease

The present status of our knowledge of the sequence of ribonuclease has been reviewed in an earlier chapter together with a consideration of some of the physical properties of this enzyme, both in its native state and under denaturing conditions. With this background we can now examine some of the covalent and noncovalent aspects of its structure in connection with the problem of catalytic activity. As we have seen, the protein contains two rather longish "tails," one at the N-terminal end consisting of 25 residues and one at the

C-terminal end consisting of 14 (Figure 62, Chapter 5). Both of these parts of the chain have been subjected to controlled hydrolysis with proteolytic enzymes. It was first shown by F. M. Richards[9] that native ribonuclease, when digested with the bacterial enzyme subtilisin, was rapidly and specifically hydrolyzed at the Ala.Ser bond (residues 20–21) in the N-terminal "tail." The resulting derivative, in which the 20 residues of the "tail" portion were still attached to the body of the enzyme through some particularly strong noncovalent interaction, could be isolated on ion exchange columns and was shown to retain the full activity of the original protein. This active, degraded ribonuclease molecule now also contains, in addition to the N-terminal lysine residue characteristic of the native enzyme, a new N-terminal serine residue.

The C-terminal end of the chain can also be degraded without inactivation. It has been possible to remove the C-terminal valine residue by carboxypeptidase treatment, together with a fraction of the serine and alanine residues which immediately precede the valine. In such samples of degraded protein no evidence for inactivation has been observed.

The site of these noninactivating cleavages with proteolytic enzymes may be assigned to specific portions of the linear polypeptide chain. Some active products of more extensive digestion have also been described for which, unfortunately, the exact sites of cleavage cannot be pinpointed at present. Uziel, Stein, and Moore,[10] for example, have reported the isolation of active derivatives of ribonuclease which has been subjected to trypsin digestion under conditions of partial unfolding of the protein in dilute urea solutions. Similarly, Kalnitsky and Rogers[11] describe experiments using carboxypeptidase digestion in which the digesting enzyme apparently contained other proteases of unknown types which caused extensive degradation of the molecule without loss of much activity. As the analysis of these latter studies becomes more complete and it becomes possible to assign the changes that have occurred to definite parts of the polypeptide chain, we shall be able to make much more useful statements about the location and nature of the "active center" of this enzyme.

We may also derive useful information from experiments designed to determine the minimum changes necessary to cause *inactivation* of the enzyme. Two particular experiments are of special interest here. The first has to do with the inactivation of ribonuclease activity during photooxidation. Weil and Seibles[12] have shown that the enzyme, when exposed to light in the presence of methylene blue, undergoes slow loss of activity and that this loss parallels, at least during the early stages of photooxidation, the disappearance of one (possibly two) of the four histidine residues that occur in this protein. Although the exact location of the histidine residue (or residues) involved has not been determined, it should be noted that two of the four are found in the C-terminal twenty amino acids of the chain.

A second sort of inactivating treatment which may ultimately help to elucidate the chemical basis of ribonuclease activity involves pepsin digestion under carefully controlled conditions. When the enzyme is exposed to pepsin at pH values in the neighborhood of 1.8, there occurs an extremely rapid hydrolysis of what appears to be a single, particularly labile, peptide bond.[13] The macromolecular portion of the reaction mixture may be isolated on ion exchange columns and is completely devoid of activity. The only other detectable fragment is a tetrapeptide, Asp.Ala.Ser.Val, the sequence of which indicates that it was derived from the C-terminal end of the chain by the cleavage of the peptide bond following the phenylalanine residue at position 120 in the polypeptide chain (see Figure 62). It has not been possible to detect the presence of cleavages elsewhere in the inactive macromolecular derivative, and both physical studies and C-terminal amino acid analysis support the conclusion that nothing else has happened beyond this unique hydrolysis.

Since the earlier studies on the carboxypeptidase treatment indicate the nonessentiality of the three C-terminally located amino acid residues, these results with pepsin suggest that the aspartic acid residue located at position 121 has some special function in the maintenance, or mechanics, of the catalytically active center. We shall discuss this point further in connection with observations on the spectral properties of ribonuclease and its various active and inactive derivatives.

Although the combined consideration of the degradative experiments indicates that some portions of the sequence of ribonuclease have greater importance in activity than others, we cannot conclude that catalysis by this enzyme requires only a simple linear sequence of amino acids. Both oxidized ribonuclease and ribonuclease that has been converted to a random, open chain by reduction of the disulfide bridges are completely inactive. It seems very likely that one or more portions of the sequence, perhaps quite widely separated in the sense of linear distance along the chain, are essential, and that their relation to one another in space is fixed by restrictions introduced by disulfide bridges and by other bridges of a noncovalent nature.

Some recent experiments on the relation between controlled, stepwise reduction of the disulfide bridges in relation to activity are of

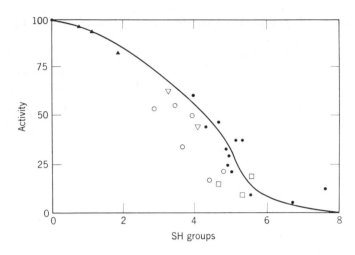

Figure 68. Activity of ribonuclease at various stages of reduction (expressed as percentage of the specific activity of native ribonuclease) as a function of the number of moles of sulfhydryl per mole of enzyme. Solid triangle, reduction in absence of urea; solid circle, reduction in 8 M urea; open square, reoxidation of fully reduced, inactive ribonuclease; open circle, reoxidation of samples containing more than six sulfhydryl groups per average molecule; open triangle, reoxidation of samples containing about four sulfhydryl groups per average molecule. From M. Sela, F. H. White, and C. B. Anfinsen, *Science*, **125**, 691 (1957).

interest in this regard.[13] The disulfide bonds may be reduced by thioglycollic acid and by various other reducing agents as discussed in Chapter 5. It has been found that the reduction of one of the four bridges in ribonuclease goes fairly rapidly in the absence of urea, but that in 8 M urea, in which the three-dimensional structure of the protein has been disoriented and "loosened," all four are easily cleaved. During reduction the activity falls off in a manner suggesting that one, and perhaps two, of the bridges may be dispensed with from the standpoint of enzymatic activity (Figure 68). Thus when an average of one SS link has been reduced, we can still demonstrate the presence of 80 to 90 per cent of the initial activity in spite of the absence of all but traces of native enzyme. Even at an average level of four SH groups per mole of protein (equivalent to the rupture of two SS bridges), considerably more than half the activity remains. It has recently been possible to separate some of the intermediates of early stages of reduction on ion exchange columns, and the identification of the bridges that are most susceptible to reductive cleavage is now under investigation. Preliminary results indicate that nearly

THE MOLECULAR BASIS OF EVOLUTION

full activity is retained after the disulfide bridge between the first and sixth half-cystine residue is cleaved.

The reduction experiments, and the proteolytic studies discussed earlier, permit us to perform a certain amount of paper surgery on the enzyme and to construct a two-dimensional picture of the maximum structural requirement for activity (Figure 69). It seems likely that amputations of other parts of this structure may be possible without inactivation. We can already safely conclude, however, that considerable portions of the covalent structure of ribonuclease must either be unimportant evolutionary vestige or involve aspects of ribonuclease function and intracellular behavior about which we are still in complete ignorance.

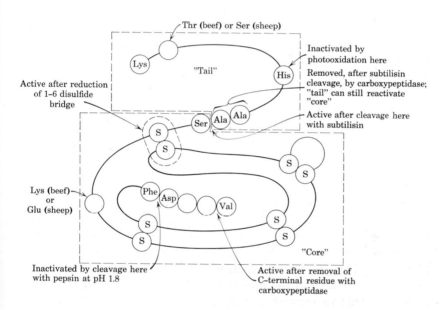

Figure 69. A schematic drawing of the ribonuclease molecule in two dimensions (see also Figure 62). Various experimental modifications of the native molecule are indicated, together with the consequences of such modifications in terms of enzyme activity. Also included are some results of studies on the comparative structures of bovine and ovine pancreatic ribonucleases (see Chapter 7). The data summarized in this figure make it tempting to suggest that much of or all the N-terminal "tail" of the molecule, together with only a portion of the "core," might eventually be shown to be sufficient for catalytic activity. The "active center" must obviously be a complicated three-dimensional structure but may not necessarily involve more than a fraction of the entire protein. This drawing is extremely speculative and is included here only to indicate some of the directions that research on the biological activity of this enzyme may take in the future.

Before leaving the subject of enzymatic structure in relation to function (and the reader must excuse my preoccupation with a specific enzyme about whose properties I happen to be able to write with less labor than certain others of equal illustrative value), let us consider a few aspects of noncovalent structure in terms of catalytic activity.[13] We have referred, in Chapter 5, to some of the physical characteristics of ribonuclease under conditions of reversible denaturation by urea. The rather large changes that occurred in the structure of the enzyme under such conditions (e.g., the intrinsic viscosity of ribonuclease in 8 M urea shifts to about 0.085 as compared with a value of 0.036 in dilute salt solution) made it of interest to examine whether or not activity was retained in 8 M urea solutions. It was quite surprising to find that hydrolysis of RNA was unimpaired and, indeed, even somewhat stimulated under these conditions of hydrogen bond disorientation. The conclusion was drawn that activity was independent of organized, three-dimensional structure. That this conclusion might be premature, however, was suggested when it was subsequently observed that low concentrations of phosphate ions or other polyvalent anions (e.g. arsenate) could reverse the unfolding effect of urea. The natural substrate for ribonuclease, RNA, is itself a polyanion and might also cause refolding of the enzyme under the conditions of assay. Various technical difficulties having to do with the spectral and optical properties of ribonucleic acid made the direct test of this hypothesis difficult. However, model substances such as polymetaphosphate and uridine-3'-phosphate (which is the product of ribonuclease attack on the synthetic substrate, uridylic-2',3'-cyclic-phosphate) could also cause a refolding of the molecule as based on measurements of its spectrum, optical rotation, and intrinsic viscosity (Table 6). The refolding was not complete, as evidenced by the somewhat lower optical rotation of the enzyme in 8 M urea in the presence of these agents as compared with that of the native enzyme in water, and by an incomplete regeneration of viscosity behavior. However, *spectral* differences were completely abolished.

Although these experiments suggested that complete "nativeness" might not be essential, as indicated by the partial but significant irreversibility of the optical rotatory and viscosity properties of the enzyme to anions, it appeared that the portion of the three-dimensional structure of the enzyme which is responsible for the peculiar spectral properties of several of the six tyrosine residues (page 120, Chapter 5) must be in the proper configuration.

In an effort to support this hypothesis, the spectra of various ac-

TABLE 6
Some Physical Properties of Ribonuclease and Modified Ribonucleases

Ribonuclease	Unfolding Agent	Anion	$\Delta_{\epsilon} . 10^{-3}$ [a]	$[\alpha]_D^{20}$	$\eta_{sp/c}$ [b]
Native	–	–	1120	−71.7°	0.036
Native	8 M urea	–	0	−103.7°	0.085
Native	8 M urea	0.4 M chloride	110	−98.8°	
Native	8 M urea	0.15 M phosphate	1120	−81.0°	0.050
Native	8 M urea	0.15 M arsenate	1120	−80.7°	
Native	8 M urea	0.15 M uridylate			0.052
Oxidized	–	–	0	−91.6°	0.116
Reduced and carboxymethylated	–	–	0		0.149
Pepsin inactivated	–	–	0	−83.8°	0.039
Subtilisin digested	–	–	1120		

The concentration of the proteins was 2.5–2.7 grams/liter for spectrophotometric readings, 25–30 grams/liter for polarimetric, and 14–15 grams/liter for viscosimetric measurements. All measurements were carried out at pH 6–7. Anions were added as their sodium salts.

The active derivative of ribonuclease produced by limited subtilisin digestion was purified according to Richards (see page 132).

[a] Change in extinction relative to the absorption of ribonuclease in 8 M urea in the absence of salts, at 285 mμ.

[b] Reduced viscosity, in $(grams/100 \ ml)^{-1}$. All viscosity measurements were carried out in 0.1 M KCl.

tive and inactive derivatives of ribonuclease were examined. It was found that all the derivatives of ribonuclease that possessed activity showed a normal "shifted' 'spectrum, whereas all those that were inactive possessed the spectral characteristics of tyrosine residues with unmodified resonance properties. We might tentatively conclude from these studies that the presence of a shifted, "native," spectrum leads to a "diagnosis" of catalytic activity and that factors which cause changes in the spectrum may be expected to inactivate.

To summarize our impressions at this point, it appears that at least one bond in the N-terminal and part of the C-terminal "tail" are dispensable, and that one, and perhaps two, of the SS bridges may be opened with impunity. Various findings suggest that a part of the structure in the vicinity of the C-terminal "tail" has special importance, specifically the aspartic acid residue at position 121. Finally, there appears to be good correlation between the presence of a "shifted" spectrum, as occurs in the native enzyme, and activity. Since the evidence is now rather convincing that such shifted spectra may involve hydrogen bonding between carboxylate groups in the protein and hydroxyl groups on tyrosine residues, it may be suggested, as one alternative, that the free carboxylate group of the aspartic acid residue at position 121 is involved in such a linkage and functions as one of the determinants of the three-dimensional form of the active center of the enzyme.

The importance of considering the enzymatic activity of a protein in terms of three-dimensional structure is strongly emphasized by an especially intriguing aspect of ribonuclease chemistry, recently reported by F. M. Richards.[9] In a continuation of his studies on the enzymatically active derivative prepared by limited subtilisin digestion, he has investigated the nature of the noncovalent bond or bonds (see page 132) which hold the N-terminal "tail" peptide to the macromolecular portion of the protein. The attachment may be broken by treatment of the derivative with trichloroacetic acid, and the N-terminal peptide fragment may be separated by dialysis and purified by electrophoretic methods. Richards has shown that both the peptide and the macromolecular component are inactive, but that upon mixing the two activity is completely regenerated as shown in Figure 70.

Richards has also examined the spectral properties of the separate fragments and of the reconstituted, active mixture. The 20-amino acid peptide, which contains no tyrosine, of course shows no absorption at 280 mμ. The large piece, however, has the expected absorption in this region of the ultraviolet, but *shows none of the spectral shift* observed with the native protein or with the subtilisin-digested enzyme before separation of the two fragments. Its spectrum is extremely similar to that observed for native ribonuclease in urea or after treatment with inactivating reagents such as pepsin. Upon mixing the two components, the shifted tyrosine spectrum reappears almost completely, indicating that the peptide "tail" plays an important part in the determination of that part of the three-dimensional structure of the protein which is responsible for the anomalous tyrosine absorption.

We have, in Richards' experiments, an instance of biological function in a relatively small peptide which is strongly reminiscent of the action of some of the peptide hormones of the anterior and posterior

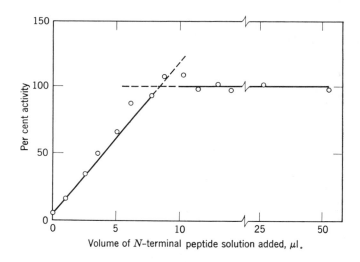

Figure 70. The regeneration of ribonuclease activity by the addition of the *N*-terminal peptide (which is split off from the native molecule by subtilisin) to the inactive macromolecular "core." As described in the text, the "core" was precipitated from the subtilisin digest with trichloroacetic acid. The *N*-terminal polypeptide, containing twenty amino acid residues, causes complete regeneration of activity when it has been added in amounts approximately equimolar with the concentration of the macromolecular component. From F. M. Richards, *Proc. Soc. Natl. Acad. Sci. U.S.*, **44**, 162 (1958).

parts of the pituitary gland. The complete regeneration of ribonuclease activity occurs at concentrations of the order of 10^{-6} *M*, a level within quite reasonable limits for hormonal action. On the basis of these studies alone, the *N*-terminal peptide fragment does not necessarily have to be an intrinsic part of the active center. It may conceivably function only as a determinant of proper folding in the rest of the molecule. Whatever its role, the forces that bind this small polypeptide to the body of ribonuclease must be multiple and highly specific.

In addition to being an essential partner to the catalytic "center" of ribonuclease, Richards' peptide fragment also appears to possess the ability to stabilize the rest of the molecule. The active subtilisin derivative is stable in aqueous solution, reflecting the considerable strength of the association between the two components of the complex. In urea, however, where these components dissociate, as they do in trichloroacetic acid, the macromolecular fraction is rapidly denatured and cannot be reactivated by the addition of the peptide, even following removal of the dissociating agent. The specific, catalytically active configuration in the intact subtilisin derivative is thus dependent on the participation of certain bonds and amino acid residues contributed by the macromolecular body of the derivative, stabilized by the peptide "tail" fragment.

It is much too early to attempt to synthesize the various observations on the chemical basis of ribonuclease into a coherent whole. It is a tribute to the progress of modern protein chemistry, however, that we can even hope to do so in the near future. The pattern already emerging for ribonuclease, in which certain widely separated areas of the protein are strongly implicated as components of an active center, and other portions (at least one disulfide bond and an assortment of amino acid residues at various points in the chain) are not, is an object lesson in the necessity for reorienting our thinking about proteins from planar to solid geometry.

REFERENCES

1. Described in *Crystalline Enzymes,* John H. Northrop, Moses Kunitz, and Roger M. Herriott, second edition, Columbia University Press, New York, 1948.
2. J. Lens, *Biochim. et Biophys. Acta,* 3, 367 (1949).
3. P. H. Bell, K. S. Howard, R. G. Shepherd, B. M. Finn, and J. H. Meisenhelder, *J. Am. Chem. Soc.* 78, 5059 (1956).
4. W. F. White and A. M. Gross, *J. Am. Chem. Soc.,* 79, 1141 (1957).
5. K. Hofmann, T. A. Thompson, and E. T. Schwartz, *J. Am. Chem. Soc.,* 79, 6087 (1957).
6. R. A. Boissonnas, S. Guttmann, J. P. Waller, and P. A. Jaquenoud, *Experientia,* 12, 446 (1956).
7. E. L. Smith, *Federation Proc.,* 16, 801 (1957).
8. R. L. Hill and E. L. Smith, *Biochim. et Biophys. Acta,* 19, 376 (1956).
9. F. M. Richards, *Proc. Natl. Acad. Sci. U.S.,* 44, 162 (1958).
10. M. Uziel, W. H. Stein, and S. Moore, *Federation Proc.,* 16, 263 (1957).
11. G. Kalnitsky and W. I. Rogers, *Biochim. et Biophys. Acta,* 20, 378 (1956).
12. L. Weil and T. S. Seibles, *Arch. Biochem. Biophys.,* 54, 368 (1955).
13. C. B. Anfinsen, *Federation Proc.,* 16, 783 (1957); M. Sela and C. B. Anfinsen, *Biochim. et Biophys. Acta,* 24, 229 (1957); M. Sela, C. B. Anfinsen, and W. F. Harrington, *Biochim. et Biophys. Acta.* 26, 502 (1957); M. Sela, F. H. White, Jr., and C. B. Anfinsen, *Science,* 125, 691 (1957).

SUGGESTIONS FOR FURTHER READING

Anfinsen, C. B., and R. R. Redfield in *Advances in Protein Chemistry,* volume 11, Academic Press, New York, 1956.

Enzymes: Units of Biological Structure and Function (O. H. Gaebler, editor), Academic Press, New York, 1956.

Molecular Structure and Biological Specificity, edited by L. Pauling and H. A. Itano, Publication 2, American Institute of Biological Sciences, Washington, D. C., 1957.

Symposium on Protein Structure (A. Neuberger, editor), John Wiley & Sons, New York, 1958.

chapter **7**

SPECIES VARIATION

IN

PROTEIN STRUCTURE

O͟ne of the major questions to be answered in ar-
riving at a clear understanding of the phylogenetic relationships between different forms of life is whether there exist identical, or
closely *homologous,* genes in widely separated species, or whether
similarities in phenotype are due to *analogous* genes which determine
equivalent appearance or function by different pathways. The techniques of experimental genetics permit us to compare the genetic
makeup of only those organisms that can be successfully crossed.
We know, for example, that the eye pigments of a wide variety of
species contain the same light-sensitive compound. However, we
have no genetic way of testing whether the synthesis of this compound in different organisms is under the control of the same set of
genes, structurally modified perhaps in some slight manner but still
essentially identical, or whether completely different genes are involved which act in concert to achieve the same end result.

All genetic analyses depend on the availability of some recogniz-
able phenotypic character, be it morphological, functional, or meta-

bolic. When the character being used as the criterion for the presence or absence of a functional gene or set of genes is a gross morphological one, we cannot attempt to distinguish homology of genes from analogy of genes. This is true even in those instances in which we can demonstrate the presence, in widely separated species, of identical chemical structures such as the creatine phosphate in the tissues of all vertebrates. The production of such a substance could be carried out by analogous, rather than homologous, enzyme systems in the different species, and the genes that exert the basic control on the synthetic process might conceivably be quite different in terms of chemical organization. There does appear to be one approach, however, which might give definitive information about the persistence of particular genes throughout the phyla. The techniques of isolation and structural analysis now available enable the protein chemist to make exact comparisons of proteins isolated from a wide variety of biological sources. If we accept the hypothesis that the proteins represent a primary, if perhaps a fuzzy, "print" of genetic information, we may then conclude that two organisms have the same gene, or gene set, when they both contain the same protein molecule. (Many readers will not be willing to swallow, whole, the thesis that proteins represent the *direct* translation of genetic information. We shall consider some of the arguments, pro and con, in Chapter 8.)

It is clear that we must expect to find differences between the "same" protein in various species. This is particularly true since, as we have discussed in the past chapter, certain parts of biologically active protein molecules are relatively more "dispensable" than others from the standpoint of function. Mutations that lead to changes in the sequence of amino acids in the last three C-terminal amino acids of ribonuclease, for example, might cause little change in the life expectancy or fertility of the affected animal. On the other hand, a mutation that led to a critical modification in the sequence of the "active center" of the enzyme might well be lethal, and the gene, so mutated, would not be perpetuated.

A comparison of the structures of homologous proteins (i.e., proteins with the same kinds of biological activity or function) from different species is important, therefore, for two reasons. First, the *similarities* found give a measure of the minimum structure which is essential for biological function. Second, the *differences* found may give us important clues to the rate at which successful mutations have occurred throughout evolutionary time and may also serve as an additional basis for establishing phylogenetic relationships.

The proteins and polypeptides for which *complete* comparisons of covalent structure can be made at the present time are relatively few in number. We can list, in this category, insulin, adrenocorticotropin, melanotropin, vasopressin, oxytocin, and hypertensin. The complete structure of glucagon (hypoglycemic factor) has been elucidated, but no comparisons of this hormone from different species have as yet appeared. Among the enzymes, only ribonuclease has been sufficiently studied to permit essentially complete comparison of species differences. The structure of a tetradecapeptide portion of cytochrome c, in the vicinity of the heme prosthetic group, has been examined for a fairly large number of organisms. Finally, there exists a large literature on the composition, end group, and end sequence analysis of various sets of homologous proteins, and on their physical, enzymatic, and immunologic properties, which allows us to make at least some educated guesses about similarities and differences.

Ribonuclease and the "Fingerprinting" Technique

The detection and study of chemical differences between homologous proteins is generally carried out by one or another variety of "fingerprinting" technique. In essence, this involves the use of reproducible physical methods for the separation of peptide fragments produced by digestion of the proteins with proteolytic enzymes. After establishing the distribution pattern of these fragments for the original "reference standard" protein, differences obtained on digests of the protein from other biological sources may then be easily detected, and the nature of the chemical modification may be determined by classical methods of amino acid and sequence analysis. An example of a "fingerprint" comparison is presented in Figures 71 and 72. This figure shows the patterns for beef and sheep ribonucleases. The differences are quite clear and are completely reproducible from digest to digest. In this instance, digestion was carried out first with trypsin and subsequently with chymotrypsin. The protein was oxidized with performic acid prior to digestion to avoid steric complications which might be introduced by the disulfide bridges.

The sort of fingerprinting used here is rapid and technically simple and serves, adequately, for the preliminary detection of differences. Indeed, if we are happy with micro techniques of the sort that served Sanger and his colleagues so well in their studies of insulin structure, a complete comparison of the corresponding peptides

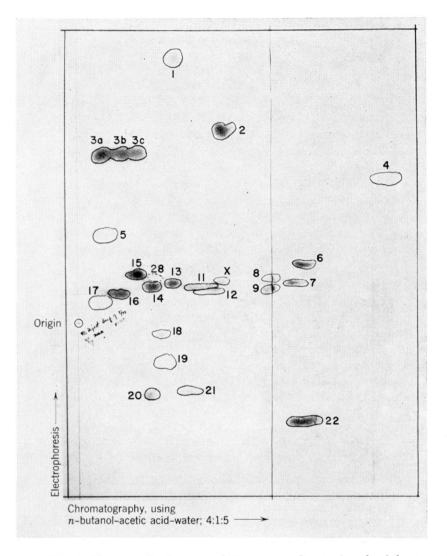

Figure 71. A "fingerprint" of a proteolytic enzyme digest of oxidized bovine pancreatic ribonuclease. An aliquot of the digest was applied in a small spot at the left of the figure. This material was then subjected to descending paper chromatography, as indicated by the arrow, and, after allowing the solvent to evaporate, the paper was moistened with buffer solution and subjected to high-voltage electrophoresis. The sheet of paper was then sprayed with ninhydrin solution to stain those areas containing peptides. These areas were cut out (from a lightly stained paper), and the peptides were eluted. The amino acid composition of each was determined, after hydrolysis with acid, by paper chromatography. The composition of the various peptide components is given in Table 8. For further details consult an article by C. B. Anfinsen, S. E. G. Åqvist, Juanita P. Cooke, and Börje Jönsson, *J. Biol. Chem.*, **234**, No. 5 (1959).

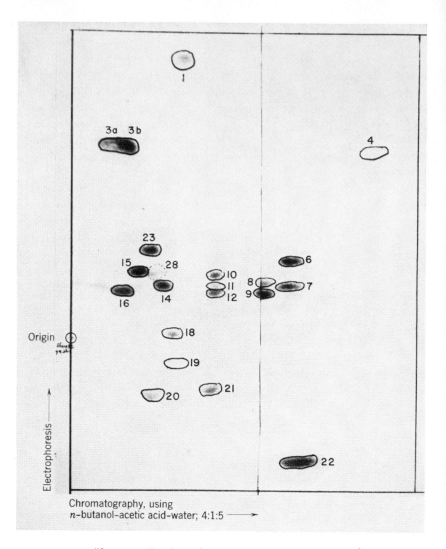

Figure 72. A "fingerprint" of performic acid-oxidized ovine pancreatic ribonuclease. The techniques employed were the same as those described in Figure 71, and the composition of the various peptide components is given in Table 8.

shown in such a fingerprint can be made with relative assurance. The use of such methods always involves an uncertainty in regard to the minor ninhydrin-positive components that routinely plague the paper chromatographer, and a certain amount of personal judgment is frequently involved in deciding whether a trace peptide compo-

THE MOLECULAR BASIS OF EVOLUTION

nent is due to a fleck of dirt on the paper or to a bona fide structural fragment. For this reason the purist will often prefer the use of ion exchange columns over paper chromatography and electrophoresis, since he can then make more quantitative estimates of the recovery of fragments in relation to theoretical expectation. The latter course is obviously to be recommended in principle. However, when a large series of proteins are to be compared, and when experience has indicated the limits of error involved, the more rapid and flexible paper method will probably be employed to establish the major generalities of structure.

The study of species differences in the structure of enzymes is of special interest because with these proteins we can, in many instances, consider such variations in terms of the ability of the enzyme to catalyze a specific, chemical reaction. When, for example, a suc-

TABLE 7

Amino Acid Analyses of Beef and Sheep Pancreatic Ribonuclease[a]

Amino Acid	"Theory"	Beef Enzyme	Sheep Enzyme	
		Average Observed Number of Residues per Mole (mol. wt. 13,683)	Average Observed Number of Residues per Mole (mol. wt. 13,683)	Estimated Changes in Sheep Enzyme
Asp	15	15.65	15.20	−1 (?)
Thr	10	9.77	9.06	−1
Ser	15	13.95	16.15	+2
Glu	12	11.75	13.3	+1 to +2
Pro	4	3.95	3.96	
Gly	3	3.03	3.14	
Ala	12	11.87	11.1	−1
Cys	4	3.36	3.66	
Val	9	8.48	8.87	
Met	4	3.62	3.73	
Ileu	3	1.83	1.76	
Leu	2	2.05	1.99	
Tyr	6	5.7	5.71	
Phe	3	3.27	3.41	
Lys	10	11.25	9.88	−1
His	4	3.51	3.83	
Arg	4	3.76	3.78	

[a] From unpublished experiments of S. Åqvist, C. B. Anfinsen, J. Cooke, and B. Jönsson.

TABLE 8
Analyses of Peptides from Fingerprints of Trypsin and Chymotrypsin Digestions of Oxidized Pancreatic Beef and Sheep Ribonuclease[a]

Beef No.	Composition		Sheep No.
3b	Lys_2,Glu,Thr,Ala_3	(beef)	–
–	Lys,Glu,Ser,Ala	(sheep)	3a and 3b
6[b]	Phe+Glu,Arg.		6[b]
–[c]	Asp,Glu,Thr,Ser_3,Met,His		–[c]
–[c]	Asp,Ala_2,Ser_3,Tyr		–[c]
16	Cys,Asp,Glu,Met_2,Lys		16
1	Ser,Arg		1
2	Asp,Leu,Thr,Lys		–
13	Asp,Arg		–
–	Asp,Leu,Thr,Glu,Arg	(sheep)	10
9	Cys,Asp,Val,Pro,Thr,Lys,Phe		9
18	Glu_3,Val_3,Leu,Ser_2,His,Asp,Ala_2,Cys		18
14	Asp,Cys,Ala,Val,Lys		14
20	Cys,Asp_2,Glu,Gly,Thr,Tyr		20
7	Glu,Ser,Tyr		7
12	Thr,Ser,Met		12
21	Cys,Asp,Ileu,Thr,Ser,Arg		21
15	Glu,Gly,Ser_2,Thr,Lys		15
8[b]	Cys,Asp,Ala,Tyr_2,Pro,Lys		8[b]
3c	Asp,Glu,Ala,Thr_2,Lys		–
–	Lys,Glu,Ala,Thr		23
28	His,Val,$Ileu_2$,Cys,Asp,Glu,Gly,Ala,Pro,Tyr		28
4	Val_2,Pro,His,Phe		4
22	Asp,Ala,Ser,Val		22
From carbobenzoxy-oxidized sheep ribonuclease	Lys,Ser,Glu,Ala,Phe,Arg		S3
	Cys,Lys,His,Asp,Glu,Ser,Met,Thr,Ala,Tyr,Arg		S1

[a] Amide nitrogens cannot be assigned to specific glutamic or aspartic acid residues since they are split off by the acid hydrolysis prior to chromatography.

[b] According to earlier observations (see Figure 60, Chapter 5), cleavages should have occurred between phenylalanine and glutamic acid in peptide 6 and in such a way as to remove the lysine residue from peptide 8. However, only traces of free phenylalanine and lysine were detected on the fingerprint patterns.

[c] These two peptides were not detected by the ninhydrin-staining reaction but have been accounted for in peptide S1, which was prepared by trypsin digestion of the carbobenzoxylated polypeptide chain (see Chapter 5), rather than by combined trypsin-chymotrypsin digestion of oxidized ribonuclease.

The spots labeled 5 and 17 in the fingerprint of digests of beef ribonuclease were present in such small quantities that their amino acid compositions could not be determined with any assurance. The same was true for the component labeled "X" in the beef ribonuclease fingerprint.

The amino acids on the paper chromatograms (Figure 73) which gave an unusually strong ninhydrin reaction are italicized. The subscripts, when present, indicate the number of moles of each amino acid in the peptide under consideration, as cessful mutation has occurred which leads to the substitution of a charged amino acid residue for an uncharged one in a sequence, this information permits us to make some helpful conclusions regarding the nature and location of the binding site for substrate molecules on the enzyme surface.

The amino acid analyses for bovine and sheep pancreatic ribonuclease are shown in Table 7. These data show that sheep ribonuclease contains less lysine, threonine (and perhaps less aspartic acid), and more serine and glutamic acid than does the beef enzyme. End group analysis indicates that both proteins contain N-terminal lysine, and sedimentation constants determined in the ultracentrifuge are essentially identical. When the peptides separated by the fingerprinting procedure illustrated in Figures 71 and 72 were eluted and analyzed, qualitatively, for amino acid composition, the results summarized in Table 8 were obtained. Examples of the chromatographic comparison of hydrolysates of a few sheep and beef peptides are shown in Figure 73. The peptides obtained from hydrolysates of the beef protein are those to be expected from the combined action of trypsin and chymotrypsin on oxidized ribonuclease, as may be deduced from the partial formula for this polypeptide shown in Figure 60. Corresponding peptides from the sheep material are also easily assignable to particular areas of the formula. Those sequences in sheep ribonuclease which differ from the beef structure may be allocated to specific areas of the chain on the basis of their compositions. At one point in the chain of the sheep enzyme, the absence of a trypsin-sensitive sequence involving lysine had precluded cleavage where the beef enzyme *was* split, and a single, longer peptide (sheep peptide 10 Figure 73e), embodying two of the beef fragments, resulted.

The studies relating various aspects of structure to function which were reviewed in the last chapter have suggested that the disulfide bridge joining half-cystines 1 and 6 may be reduced without complete destruction of catalytic activity. The species variation occurring at residue 37, where a positively charged amino acid, lysine, has been replaced by a negatively charged amino acid, glutamic acid, also suggests the unessentiality for substrate adsorption and hydrolysis of this part of the polypeptide chain.

---

determined for beef ribonuclease (Figure 60, Chapter 5). Thus for beef peptide 3b the earlier quantitative analyses, which demonstrated the presence of two residues of lysine and three of alanine for each residue of glutamic acid and threonine, were confirmed by the staining reaction which was correspondingly stronger for the two former amino acids.

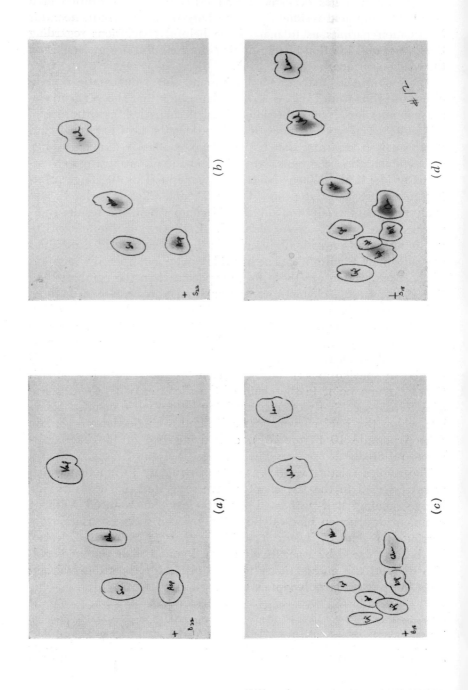

(a)

(b)

(c)

(d)

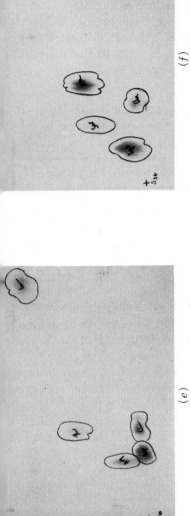

(e)

(g)

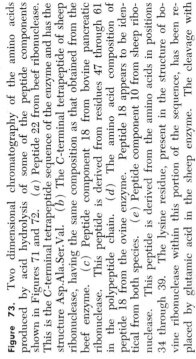

(f)

Figure 73. Two dimensional chromatography of the amino acids produced by acid hydrolysis of some of the peptide components shown in Figures 71 and 72. (*a*) Peptide 22 from beef ribonuclease. This is the *C*-terminal tetrapeptide sequence of the enzyme and has the structure Asp.Ala.Ser.Val. (*b*) The *C*-terminal tetrapeptide of sheep ribonuclease, having the same composition as that obtained from the beef enzyme. (*c*) Peptide component 18 from bovine pancreatic ribonuclease. This peptide is derived from residues 47 through 61 in the polypeptide chain. (*d*) The amino acid composition of peptide 18 from the ovine enzyme. Peptide 18 appears to be identical from both species. (*e*) Peptide component 10 from sheep ribonuclease. This peptide is derived from the amino acids in positions 34 through 39. The lysine residue, present in the structure of bovine ribonuclease within this portion of the sequence, has been replaced by glutamic acid in the sheep enzyme. The cleavage with trypsin which occurs at residue 37 of the beef enzyme can thus not occur for the sheep protein, and a single hexapeptide sequence is obtained instead of a tetrapeptide and dipeptide. (*f*) Peptide component 3b from sheep ribonuclease. The peptide represents the *N*-terminal heptapeptide sequence of the enzyme. (*g*) Component 3b from the beef fingerprint, the *N*-terminal heptapeptide *sequence*. The beef enzyme differs, in this region, from the sheep enzyme by the replacement of serine by threonine. See Figure 62 for details of structure.

Adrenocorticotropin (ACTH)

The complete amino acid sequences are known for corticotropins isolated from the anterior pituitary glands of three different species, pig, beef, and sheep. The structure of sheep ACTH was discussed in the last chapter, and the sequences shown in Table 9 include only those areas of the three molecules where differences are to be found. Although some difference between the content of amide nitrogen groups has been reported for the three species, these are not included in the figure since it has not been possible to rule out, with certainty, the possibility that these variations are due, in part, to the rigors of the isolation and purification techniques employed.

TABLE 9

Variations in Amino Acid Sequences Among Different Preparations of ACTH

		Residue No.								
Preparation	Species	25	26	27	28	29	30	31	32	33
β-Corticotropin	sheep⎫ beef[a]⎭	Ala.Gly.Glu.Asp.Asp.Glu						Ala.Ser.Glu.NH₂		
Corticotropin A	pig	Asp.Gly.Ala.Glu.Asp.Glu						Leu.Ala.Glu		

[a] Identity with sheep hormone not absolutely certain but very probable as judged from the nearly complete sequence analysis by J. S. Dixon and C. H. Li (personal communication to the author).

Two points are of particular interest in regard to the sequences shown. First, the corticotropins of sheep and beef are identical and differ from that of the pig. This finding is consonant with the closer phylogenetic relationship of sheep and cows to each other than of either to pigs. Second, chemical differences are found only in that portion of the ACTH molecule which has been shown to be unessential for hormonal activity. Genetic mutations leading to such differences might, therefore, not be expected to impose significant disadvantages in terms of survival, and these genes could become established in the gene pools of the species.

Melanotropin (MSH)

Melanotropin, like the other hormones considered in this chapter, is a typically chordate polypeptide. Indeed, the demonstration of melanocyte-stimulating activity in extracts of tunicates constitutes an

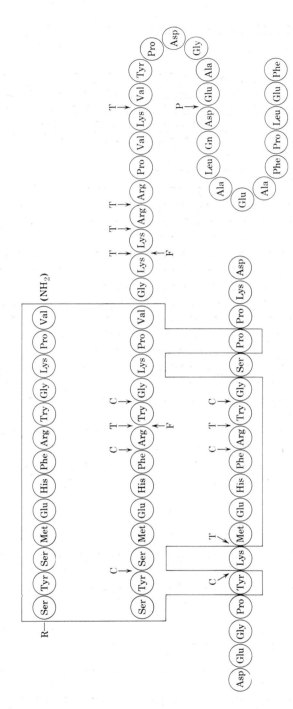

Figure 74. The structures of porcine α-ACTH (center), α-MSH (lower), and β-MSH (upper). Points of cleavage by chymotrypsin (C), trypsin (T), pepsin (P), and fibrinolysin (F) are indicated by the arrows. The common sequences are indicated within the boxed area.

important bit of evidence supporting the assignment of these organisms to the main thoroughfare of evolution between invertebrates and chordates.

Melanotropins have been isolated in pure form from both pig and beef pituitaries (posterior-intermediate lobes). Only a single polypeptide having MSH activity has been isolated from beef tissues, whereas two different chemical entities termed α and β-MSH have been isolated and characterized from hog pituitaries. The structures of these substances is given in Figure 74 together with that for porcine ACTH. We shall consider further the provocative similarity between the structures of MSH and ACTH in Chapter 10 in relation to protein biosynthesis. This similarity is undoubtedly responsible for the fact that adrenocorticotropic hormone exhibits marked melanocyte-stimulating activity.

Beef β-MSH differs from porcine β-MSH only in the replacement of the glutamic acid residue in position 2 by serine. Porcine α-MSH, however, is considerably different from both the other hormones and is actually identical with the sequence of the first thirteen amino acids in pig ACTH, except for the presence of a masking, acyl, group on the N-terminal amino group and an amide nitrogen group at the C-terminus. Lee and Lerner,[1] who isolated α-MSH, have suggested that this form of the hormone is the major one in pituitary extracts since it accounts, in their experiments, for the largest share of activity, although other investigators have not so far confirmed the presence of α-MSH.*

Bovine β-MSH possesses considerably less biological activity than does porcine β-MSH, and, until comparisons can be made of synthetic samples of these two materials, this difference in potency must be ascribed to the amino acid substitution at position 2.

Insulin

Sanger and his colleagues have determined the amino acid sequences for insulins derived from five different species. Differences

* C. H. Li and his colleagues have also recently isolated α-MSH from both porcine and bovine pituitary glands. The structures were found to be the same in both species. (Personal communication.)

The sequence of α-MSH has been confirmed by total synthesis in the laboratories of Klaus Hofmann and of R. Boissonnas. The activity of the synthetic material is critically dependent on the presence of the acetyl group on the N-terminal serine residue. Thus, in the experiments of Boissonnas and his coworkers, the activity of the acetylated polypeptide was approximately 70 times greater than before acetylation. (Personal communications from Hofmann and Boissonnas.)

　　　　　　　　　　　　　　　　THE MOLECULAR BASIS OF EVOLUTION

```
. . . CySO₃H.Ala.Ser.Val . . . (beef)
. . . CySO₃H.Thr.Ser.Ileu . . . (pig)
. . . CySO₃H.Ala.Gly.Val . . . (sheep)
. . . CySO₃H.Thr.Gly.Ileu . . . (horse)
. . . CySO₃H.Thr.Ser.Ileu . . . (sperm whale)
. . . CySO₃H.Ala.Ser.Thr . . . (sei whale)
```

Figure 75. Species differences in the amino acid sequences of insulins from various biological sources. These differences all occur within the disulfide "loop" of the A chain.

were limited to the amino acids within the disulfide "loop" of the A chain (Figure 75) and the B chain was identical in all instances (see Figure 65). Of the five insulins examined, only those from the pig and the sperm whale exhibited the same structure. The fact that all the observed differences were restricted to the sequence within the "loop" suggests that the amino acids in this region of the insulin molecule are not particularly critical ones from the standpoint of hormonal activity. On the other hand, several investigators have obtained evidence indicating that insulin loses its biological activity when disulfide bridges are reductively cleaved. The species difference results with insulin suggest that only the steric configuration of the loop is essential and that the "spacers" between the half-cystine residues may be varied through mutation of the corresponding gene or genes. It is of interest that sequence variations have *not* been observed in the C-terminal region of the B chain, an area which does appear to be essential for activity as shown by the inactivation of insulin following the removal of the last seven residues in the chain.

Hypertensins

The hypertensins are peptides present in serum which possess pressor activity. Two forms have been isolated from horse serum,[2] the first being convertible to the second by the action of an enzyme in plasma according to the equation:

Asp.Arg.Val.Tyr.Ileu.His.Pro.Phe.His.Leu →
    Asp.Arg.Val.Tyr.Ileu.His.Pro.Phe. + His.Leu

The precursor compound is not active in an *in vitro* test system, but after cleavage of the critical peptide bond it becomes active both *in vivo* and *in vitro*. The precursor form has also been isolated from

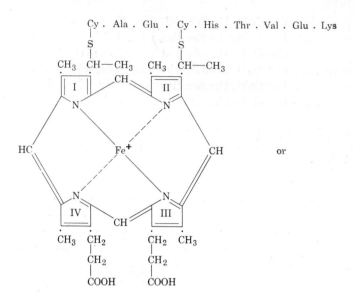

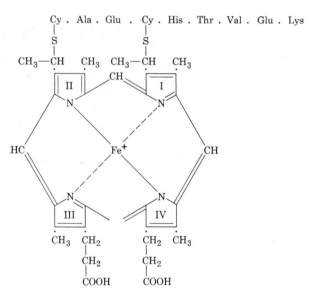

Figure 76. Structure of the peptide-porphyrin compound isolated from trypsin digests of cytochrome c. After H. Tuppy and G. Bodo, *Monatsch. Chem.,* **85,** 1024 (1954).

bovine serum[3] and is identical with that from horse serum except for the substitution of *isoleucine by valine*. These two amino acids are extremely similar in structure and the substitution in this case represents one of the more minimal changes possible given the available selection of naturally occurring amino acids.

Cytochrome c

The electron-transporting enzyme, cytochrome c, furnishes one of the most interesting examples of species variations in protein structure, since it has been isolated in pure form from a particularly wide assortment of species. Unfortunately, studies on variations in sequence have been carried out for only a relatively small portion of the total chain, and preliminary amino acid analyses indicate that there may be modifications elsewhere in the molecule as well. Never-

Beef
Horse $\overset{\displaystyle NH_2}{|}$ $\overset{\displaystyle NH_2}{|}$
Pig   . . . Val.Glu.Lys.Cys.Ala.Glu.Cys.His.Thr.Val.Glu.Lys . . .

Salmon $\overset{\displaystyle NH_2}{|}$ $\overset{\displaystyle NH_2}{|}$
     . . . Val.Glu.Lys.Cys.Ala.Glu.Cys.His.Thr.Val.Glu . . .

Chicken $\overset{\displaystyle NH_2}{|}$ $\overset{\displaystyle NH_2}{|}$
     . . . Val.Glu.Lys.Cys.Ser.Glu.Cys.His.Thr.Val.Glu . . .

Silkworm $\overset{\displaystyle NH_2}{|}$ $\overset{\displaystyle NH_2}{|}$
     . . . Val.Glu.Arg.Cys.Ala.Glu.Cys.His.Thr.Val.Glu . . .

Yeast   Phe.Lys.Thr.Arg.Cys.Glu.Leu.Cys.His.Thr.Val.Glu . . .

Rhodospiril-   . . . Lys ⎫
lum rubrum   or ⎬ .Cys.Leu.Ala.Cys.His.Thr.Phe.Asp.Glu.Gly.Ala.Asp.Lys . . .
     Arg ⎭ $\overset{\displaystyle NH_2}{|}$

                                    Lys ⎫
Common sequence: or ⎬ .Cys.X.Y.Cys.His.Thr.
                                    Arg ⎭

Figure 77. Variations in the sequence of the polypeptide chain of cytochrome c from species to species. From H. Tuppy, *Symposium on Protein Structure* (A. Neuberger, editor), John Wiley & Sons, 1958.

theless, the investigations of H. Tuppy, S. Paléus, and G. Bodo,[4] on this ubiquitously distributed enzyme, lend the most convincing support to the argument that certain units of the universal gene pool may be extremely ancient.

In the degradative studies of the enzyme, advantage was taken of the finding of H. Theorell[5] that the heme prosthetic group of cytochrome c is attached through stable thioether linkages to the protein moiety. After proteolytic degradation with trypsin (and in later studies with pepsin), that portion of the polypeptide chain which is attached to the heme nucleus was isolated. The structure of the heme-peptide compound as determined for cytochrome c from horse heart tissue is shown (in two alternatively possible forms) in Figure 76.

In subsequent investigations corresponding sequences from cytochrome obtained from a variety of other species have been elucidated as shown in Figure 77.

Somatotropins (Growth Hormones) and Prolactin

Pure growth hormone has been isolated from the pituitaries of the species listed in Table 10 by C. H. Li and his colleagues. These proteins have been subjected to both physical and chemical study, and, although even partially complete sequences are not yet available, a great deal can already be said about species variability. Molecular weights vary over nearly a twofold range, and the differences in the number of chains and the cystine content are striking. The beef and sheep hormones are, as in the case of several other proteins we have discussed earlier, quite similar, reflecting once again the close phylogenetic relationship between these two species.

The prolactins of sheep and beef are also extremely similar (Table 11), the only difference between them so far observed being a slightly greater tyrosine content in the beef hormone. The absence of a chemically detectable C-terminal amino acid residue is another example of "masked" end groups. The nature of the masking is unknown.

Hemoglobin

The hemoglobins have been studied, from the phylogenetic point of view, perhaps more than any other class of proteins. Most of

TABLE 10

N- and C-Terminal Sequences of Somatotropins from Various Species[a]

Terminal Sequences

Somatotropins	Amino End	Carboxyl End
Bovine	Phe.Ala . . . Ala.Phe.Ala . . .	. . . Ala.Phe.Phe
Ovine	Phe . . . Ala . . .	. . . Try.Ala.Phe
Whale	Phe.AspNH$_2$.Lys . . .	. . . Leu.Ala.Phe
Monkey	Phe.Ala.Thr . . .	. . . Ala.Gly.Phe
Human	Phe.Ser.Thr . . .	. . . Tyr.Leu.Phe

Some Physicochemical Properties of Various Somatotropins

Physicochemical Characteristics[b]	Bovine	Ovine	Whale	Monkey	Human
$S_{20,w}$	3.19	2.76	2.84	1.88	2.47
$D_{20,w} \times 10^7$	7.23	5.25	6.56	7.20	8.88
V_{20}	0.76	0.733	0.737	0.726	0.732
Molecular weight	45,000	47,800	39,900	25,400	27,100
f/f_0	1.31	1.68	1.45	1.57	1.23
P_I	6.85	6.8	6.2	5.5	4.9
Cystine	4	5	3	4	2
N-Terminal Residue(s)	Phe,Ala	Phe,Ala	Phe	Phe	Phe
C-Terminal Residue	Phe	Phe	Phe	Phe	Phe

[a] From C. H. Li, *Symposium on Protein Structure* (A. Neuberger, editor), John Wiley & Sons, 1958.

[b] $S_{20,w}$ in Svedbergs; $D_{20,w}$ in cm.^{2}/sec.; $\overline{V}$ in cc./gram; f/f_0, dissymmetry constant; P_I, isoelectric point; cystine in residues per mole. For details on the determination and significance of the physical constants consult the volumes entitled *The Proteins* (H. Neurath and K. Bailey, editors), Academic Press, 1953, 1954.

the available information on the hemoglobins has to do with the chemical and spectrophotometric characteristics of the various prosthetic groups and with oxygen and carbon dioxide-combining properties. Consequently, this information is not directly pertinent to our present discussion of species differences in protein structure. Re-

TABLE 11

Some Physical and Chemical Properties of Prolactin from Ovine and Bovine Pituitary Glands[a]

Physical and Chemical Properties	Ovine	Bovine
Molecular weight		
Sedimentation-diffusion	24,200	
Osmotic pressure	26,500	26,000
Analytical data	24,100	
Diffusion coefficient (D_{20})	8.44×10^{-7}	
Sedimentation constant ($S_{20,w}$)	2.19	
Partial specific volume (V_{20})	0.739	
Isoelectric point, pH	5.73	5.73
Specific rotation	$-40.5°$	$-40.5°$
Partition coefficient (2-butanol/0.35%		
aqueous trichloroacetic acid)	1.58	2.07
Tyrosine, %	5.26	6.62
Tryptophan, %	1.69	1.75
Cystine, residue/mole	3	3
N-terminal amino acid	Threonine	Threonine
C-terminal amino acid	none	none

[a] From C. H. Li, *Symposium on Protein Structure* (A. Neuberger, editor), John Wiley & Sons, 1958.

cently, however, following the important initial studies of R. Porter and F. Sanger,[6] a number of investigators have begun to examine amino acid sequences in the hemoglobins. Such studies are becoming increasingly more meaningful as the result of physicochemical investigations on the number of peptide chains per molecule and on the size of the monomer subunit. It now appears that, with the possible exception of foetal hemoglobin and the hemoglobin of the chicken (perhaps birds in general), the vertebrate hemoglobins contain two types of chains. These are present, under physiological conditions, in the form of a molecule with a molecular weight of about 65,000, composed of four chains, two of each type, held together through noncovalent linkages. (The earlier results, which indicated the presence of *six* chains in the hemoglobin of the horse, are probably incorrect on the basis of recent electrophoretic and ultracentrifugal investigations.) Valine is the N-terminal amino acid residue on both polypeptide chains of the vertebrate hemoglobins so far examined, except for the goat, sheep, and cow, in which one of the chains begins with methionine. A summary of the available end group data is given in Table 12. It is far too early to attempt to make any

                  THE MOLECULAR BASIS OF EVOLUTION

TABLE 12

End Group Data on Vertebrate Hemoglobins

Species	N-Terminal Amino Acids or Sequences[a]		
Human adult[1,3]	Val.Leu	Val.–	
Human foetal[1,3]	Val.–	Val.–	
Dog[2]	Val.Leu	Val.Gly	(Val.Asp)[2]
Horse,[1,2,4] pig[2]	Val.Leu	Val.Glu.Leu	(Val.Gly)[2]
Cow,[1,2] goat,[1,2] sheep[1,2]	Val.Leu	Met.Gly	
Guinea pig[2]	Val.Leu	Val.Ser	(Val.Asp)[2]
Rabbit,[2] snake[2]	Val.Leu	Val.Gly	
Chicken[2]	Val.Leu		

[a] The presence of a third N-terminal sequence has been reported only by Ozawa and Satake.[2]

1. K. Porter and F. Sanger, *Biochem. J.*, **42**, 287 (1948).
2. H. Ozawa and K. Satake, *J. Biochem. (Japan)*, **42**, 641 (1955).
3. M. S. Masri and K. Singer, *Arch. Biochem. Biophys.*, **58**, 414 (1955).
4. D. B. Smith, A. Haug, and S. Wilson, *Federation Proceedings*, **16**, 766 (1957).

evolutionary sense out of this information. However, it might be pointed out that the N-terminal sequence, Val.Leu, seems to be present throughout the species examined, including the representatives of the reptiles and the birds. We may speculate on the possibility that the "valyl-leucyl" chain represents a relatively early invention of evolution, and that the addition (and modification) of a second type of chain accompanied later differentiations in the vertebrate phylum.

The elegant studies of Pauling, Itano, and their colleagues, and of Ingram on the normal and abnormal human hemoglobins, are discussed in the next chapter. The information gained from these studies should be of great value as a baseline for the investigation of hemoglobin structure in other species.

Species Comparisons of Serum Proteins

The chemist, interested in comparative protein chemistry, generally studies proteins that have unique and interesting biological activities. This is the reason why most of our knowledge of protein structure concerns enzymes, hormones, and pigment-associated proteins. The odds in favor of being chosen for study are, in a sense, fixed in favor of exactly those proteins that Nature might find it necessary to preserve in reasonably unmodified form during the evolutionary process.

TABLE 13
Precipitin Tests with Antihuman Serum[a]

(Antihuman serum was prepared in rabbits by periodic injection
with human serum)

Origin of Serum	Amount of Precipitate Relative to Human
Primates	
Man	100
Chimpanzee	130 (loose precipitum)
Gorilla	64
Orang	42
Mandrill	42
Guinea baboon	29
Spider monkey	29
Carnivores	
Dog	3
Jackal	10 (loose precipitum)
Himalayan bear	8
Genet	3
Cat	3
Persian lynx	3
Tiger	2
Ungulates	
Ox	10
Sheep	10
Water buck	7
Hog deer	7
Reindeer	7
Goat	2
Horse	2
Swine	0
Rodents	
Guinea pig	0
Rabbit	0
Insectivores	
Tenrec	0
Marsupials	
Six species: rock and nail-tailed wallabies, kangaroo, Tasmanian wolf	0

[a] After G. H. F. Nuttall, from *Biochemical Evolution*; G. Wald in *Trends in Physiology and Biochemistry* (E. S. G. Barron, editor), Academic Press, 1952.

On the other hand, the "permissible" degree of change in proteins that require less rigid engineering, such as certain of the serum proteins, the less dynamic elements of tissues such as the collagens and elastins, and various proteins of the hair and skin, is likely to be quite large.

One of the earliest studies of the comparative biochemistry of proteins was carried out by Nuttall and his collaborators. These investigators used immunological techniques to study the phylogenetic relationships between the serum proteins of a wide variety of species. They employed the extent of the precipitin reaction between antihuman serum and the serums of other species as a measure of similarity (Table 13). We know that the precipitin reaction is not an absolutely specific one and, therefore, that cross reactions which do occur do not require the presence of molecules identical to human serum protein molecules. The results suggest that the serum proteins of the species examined form a graded series of macromolecules in which only serums from phylogenetic "neighbors" can cross react significantly. Nuttall strengthened this conclusion by cross-reacting serums from more closely related animals. A dramatic example is his observation that antifrog serum reacts strongly with serums of other tail-less amphibia, but not at all with those of tailed amphibia.

In spite of the complete lack of immunochemical similarity between the serum albumins of distant species, the more obvious functional aspects of the protein may nevertheless be retained. For example, the serum albumins of rat and man carry out such physiological functions as fatty acid binding and transport and osmotic pressure regulation, in essentially the same manner and with equal facility. We may guess, until experimentation has a chance to prove us wrong, that the modifications which led to immunological differences spared, or at least only slightly remodeled, the functionally critical parts of serum albumin structure.

REFERENCES

1. T. G. Lee and A. B. Lerner, *J. Biol. Chem.*, **221**, 943 (1956).
2. L. T. Skeggs, Jr., K. E. Lentz, J. R. Kahn, N. P. Shumway, and K. R. Woods, *J. Exptl. Med.*, **104**, 193 (1956).
3. D. F. Elliott and W. S. Peart, *Nature*, **177**, 527 (1956).
4. These studies are summarized by H. Tuppy in *Symposium on Protein Structure* (A. Neuberger, editor), Methuen, London, 1958.
5. H. Theorell, *Biochem. Z.*, **298**, 242 (1938); *Enzymologia*, **6**, 88 (1939).
6. R. R. Porter and F. Sanger, *Biochem. J.*, **42**, 287 (1948).

chapter 8

GENES AS DETERMINANTS
OF
PROTEIN STRUCTURE

Studies on the biochemical effects of mutations have given strong support to the notion that individual genes are concerned with the biosynthesis of individual proteins. In a large number of instances it has been possible to attribute the absence, or modification of an enzyme to a single gene mutation. The study of such biochemical lesions, not only in microorganisms like *Neurospora* and *E. coli* but in man and other higher organisms as well, has led to the concept of a "one gene–one enzyme" relationship, which we have already introduced in Chapter 2.

The term "gene" as used in this context has, until quite recently, been employed to convey the purely abstract concept of a unit of heredity. It represented a quantum of genetic information that in some way controlled the biosynthesis of a single protein or, in more cautious terms, of some "functional unit." The recent advances in the biochemistry of the chromosome and of DNA, and in the mapping of genetic "fine structure" of the sort we have discussed in relation to bacteriophage, now make it possible to speculate about gene action in chemical terms instead of formal abstraction. The investigations of S. Benzer, G. Streisinger, M. Demerec and his collaborators, G. Pontecorvo, and many others have indicated that the idea of a one-dimensional array of "genes," divisible by genetic recombination, may very likely be extended down to molecular dimensions. Their results suggest that the word "pseudoallelism" needed to be invented only because of the difficulties of demonstrating extremely rare recombinations in unfavorable biological material.

If we accept the generalities of the "one gene–one enzyme" concept, and if we are willing to go along with the present trend of opinion on the role of DNA as the basic determinant of heredity, we must seriously consider the conclusion that the information which governs details of protein structure is present in the chemical structure of the DNA molecule. It is an undeniable temptation to suggest further that a point mutation is really just a very localized change in the sequence or the three-dimensional relationships within a polynucleotide chain and that such a localized change might reflect itself in the sequence and folding of the protein concerned. In spite of the fact that many investigators properly accept the generality as a working hypothesis, such speculations are, at present, mostly fancy with little fact. The pathway from gene structure to phenotypic protein may be a long and tortuous one, and we cannot rule out such possible complications as the combined action of several genes in the synthesis of a single protein or the involvement of cytoplasmic hereditary factors which might modify, or even initiate, steps in a biosynthetic pathway.

If this hypothesis is an approximately correct one, however, we should, as N. Horowitz has pointed out, be able to demonstrate mutations that lead to qualitative as well as quantitative changes in enzymes and other proteins. It should be possible, for example, to show that various mutations within a given protein-determining region of the genetic material of an organism can lead to "mutant" forms of a biologically active protein which exhibit varying degrees of functional adequacy. Mutations affecting portions of protein structure that are essential for function should be lethal ones, whereas those affecting less essential regions might either be undetected or "leaky," to use the genetic patois.

In spite of the fact that hundreds of examples have been found of gene-protein relationships, it has been possible to demonstrate a correlation between the mutation of a single gene and the chemical and physical properties of a *homogeneous* protein molecule in only a few instances. Many of these positive correlations have emerged from studies on proteins of higher organisms for the simple reason that protein samples of sufficient purity are easier to come by with red cells, milk, and plasma than with microorganisms. However, the advantages offered by microorganisms in respect to genetic mapping has been a tremendous stimulus to gene-minded protein chemists, and it is likely that many of the major advances in this area will be made on material from such sources. If, for example, the protein whose biosynthesis is under the control of that region of genetic material in T4 bacteriophage so elegantly mapped by Benzer (see Chapter 4) could be identified and isolated in pure form, it is clear that a direct

TABLE 14
Alterations in Proteins Attributable to Mutations

Protein	Species	Demonstrated or Possible Effects of Mutation
Hemoglobin[1,2]	Man	Composition and charge
	Sheep	Charge
	Mouse	Charge
β-Lactoglobulin[1,2]	Cattle	Charge
Haptoglobin[2]	Man	Charge
Pantothenate-synthesizing enzyme[1]	E. coli	Thermostability
Tyrosinase[1]	Neurospora cr.	Thermostability
Glutamic acid dehydrogenase[1]	Neurospora cr.	Reversible heat activation

For more detailed reference see:
1. N. Horowitz, *Federation Proc.*, **15**, 818 (1956).
2. D. Steinberg and E. Mihalyi, *Ann. Rev. Biochem.*, **26**, 373 (1957).

test, in enormous detail, could be made for the existence of a correspondence between "cistron" and protein. Such detail could never be achieved with human proteins because extensive gene mapping in man is limited by his lengthy generation time and his eugenic mores.

A partial list of those proteins for which gene-linked modification has been demonstrated is presented in Table 14. With one exception, human hemoglobin, the difference between the normal protein and that obtained from the mutant has been in electrophoretic mobility, heat stability, and serological behavior. The net charge, stability, and serology of a protein are, of course, quite distinctive characteristics, and the proteins in Table 14 which have been studied in respect to these parameters can almost certainly be assumed to exist in forms whose differences are related to allelomorphic genes. Nevertheless, small organic molecules, tightly bound to proteins, can modify charge, and polysaccharides or other haptenic substances may influence antigenicity. For such reasons, the case of human hemoglobin is a particularly favorable one, since for this protein the electrophoretic and solubility differences between mutant forms are attributable to actual modifications in amino acid sequence.

In 1949, L. Pauling, H. A. Itano, S. J. Singer, and I. C. Wells[1] made the important observation that the hemoglobin of sickle-cell anemics is electrophoretically abnormal and that in individuals with sickle-cell trait (an asymptomatic condition) a mixture of the abnormal sickle-cell and the normal forms could be demonstrated. Extensive study of the familial relationships of sickle-cell anemia has indicated that this frequently fatal disease is inherited in a Mendelian fashion. By an analysis of the genetic relationships between sickle-cell anemia and sickle-cell trait, J. V. Neel established that the production of the abnormal hemoglobin was due to the presence of a single mutant gene. Genetically, the anemic may be characterized as homozygous for the sickling gene and the individual with the trait as heterozygous.

The studies of Pauling and Itano and their collaborators, together with the discovery by H. Hörlein and G. Weber[2] of a congenital methemoglobinemia involving an abnormal globin component, stimulated the search for other genetically linked aberrations in hemoglobin synthesis. At present writing a dozen or more types of abnormal hemoglobins which may be detected by their unusual physical properties are known. In addition, there are a number of clinical situations in which detection depends on hematologic examination but no changes in the physical properties of hemoglobin have been observed. Such abnormal individuals have microcytic red cells or cells showing some other deviation from the normal morphology of erythrocytes. These instances of inhibition of synthesis of normal hemoglobin are collectively named thalassemia, and Allison has proposed, on the basis of the observation that the locus controlling the thalassemia effect does not appear to be allelomorphic with the normal hemoglobin gene, Hb^A, that the locus for thalassemia be designated Th. The normal gene at this locus would then be termed Th^N and the thalassemia allele, Th^T.

Examples of the clinical nomenclature and genotypic designations for a number of abnormalities involving the hemoglobin molecule are given in Table 15. This compilation is taken from the excellent review by Itano to which the reader is referred for more detailed information. For our present purposes it is sufficient to recognize,

TABLE 15
The Human Hemoglobins[a]

Method of Detection		Method of Detection	
A	Normal adult	E	Electrophoresis
F	Foetal	G	Electrophoresis
X	Electrophoresis	H	Electrophoresis
S	Electrophoresis	I	Electrophoresis
	Solubility	J	Electrophoresis
	Tactoid formation	M	Spectrophotometry
C	Electrophoresis		
D	Electrophoresis and solubility		

Nomenclature of Syndromes Associated with Abnormalities in Hemoglobin Metabolism

Condition	Genotype	
	Hb Locus	Th Locus
Homozygous		
Normal	$Hb^A Hb^A$	$Th^N Th^N$
Sickle-cell anemia	$Hb^S Hb^S$	
Hemoglobin C disease	$Hb^C Hb^C$	
Thalassemia major	$Hb^{th} Hb^{th}$	
Thalassemia major		$Th^T Th^T$
Heterozygous		
Sickle-cell trait	$Hb^A Hb^S$	
Hemoglobin C trait	$Hb^A Hb^C$	
Sickle-cell hemoglobin C disease	$Hb^S Hb^C$	
Thalassemia minor	$Hb^A Hb^{th}$	
Thalassemia minor		$Th^N Th^T$
Sickle-cell thalassemia disease	$Hb^S Hb^{th}$	
Hemoglobin C thalassemia disease	$Hb^C Hb^{th}$	
Doubly heterozygous		
Sickle-cell thalassemia disease	$Hb^A Hb^S$	$Th^N Th^T$
Hemoglobin C thalassemia disease	$Hb^A Hb^C$	$Th^N Th^T$

[a] From a review by H. Itano, *Advances in Protein Chemistry*, volume 12, (C. B. Anfinsen, M. L. Anson, K. Bailey, and J. T. Edsall, editors), Academic Press, p. 215, 1957.

first, that some of the various abnormal hemoglobins (Hb^c, Hb^s, etc.) are under the control of a series of genes which seem to be allelic (they are, perhaps, pseudoallelic) and, second, that certain other abnormalities, inclusively termed thallassemias (Th^{T_1}, Th^{T_2}, etc.) involve genetic abnormalities for which no physical or chemical reflection in the structure of the hemoglobin molecule has been observed and which appear to be associated with genetic loci different from the Hb^A locus.

Let us now examine what chemical data we have. The differences observed by Pauling, Itano, and their colleagues in the electrophoretic mobility of normal and sickle-cell hemoglobin might be ascribed to modifications in the amino acid sequence leading to the introduction or deletion of charged side-chain groups. On the other hand, such charge differences might be apparent only and could reflect the manner of folding of the polypeptide chains of the protein to expose or to mask charged groups in response to configurational change. A direct test of these hypotheses has been made by V. Ingram,[3] who has examined the details of sequence in the molecule (Figure 78) by means of the sensitive "fingerprinting" technique described in the previous chapter. His investigations have made it extremely likely that both sickle-cell hemoglobin and hemoglobin C differ from normal hemoglobin in only a single amino acid residue. The affected portion of the protein is shown in Figure 79. A glutamic acid residue in Hb^A has been replaced with valine and lysine, respectively, in Hb^s and Hb^c. The corresponding changes in net charge per mole (plus 2 for Hb^s and plus 4 for Hb^c, with respect to Hb^A) agree with that to be expected from the electrophoretic measurements, and no evidence has been obtained for other changes in sequence in the rest of the molecular structure of the protein. We have here, then, a direct test of the proposition that a mutation in a specific genetic locus causes a specific change in the covalent structure of the phenotypic protein related to this locus. Indeed, Ingram's experiments are a test with a vengeance. Not only do the allelic Mendelian genes Hb^A, Hb^s, and Hb^c have to do with a very restricted aspect of structure, but they all appear to be related to the *same* aspect, namely the sequence at one unique point. If the sequence of nucleotides in the polynucleotide chain of DNA determines polypeptide sequence, how can we explain the fact that these three genetically segregatable loci all influence the same position in the polypeptide?

A particularly intriguing possibility for explaining Ingram's results comes from a consideration of the theoretical model of Watson and Crick for DNA structure. The obligatory pairing of heterocyclic

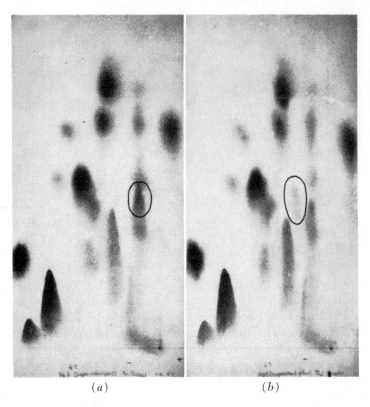

(a)   (b)

Figure 78. "Fingerprints" of the peptides produced by digestion of normal hemoglobin (a) and sickle-cell hemoglobin (b) with trypsin. The "fingerprints" were obtained by a combination of electrophoresis and chromatography, more or less as described in Figures 71 and 72. The encircled areas in the figure show where the fingerprints differ significantly. From V. M. Ingram, *Nature*, **180**, 326 (1957).

bases in this structure has, as we have discussed earlier, been suggested as a basis for the accurate self-duplication of DNA strands. The specific sequences of the bases in the complementary strands of the double helix have also been viewed as a set of coded genetic information which might serve as the fundamental template for protein synthesis. The most popular code form has been one based on "triplets," in which various sets of three nucleotides correspond to a specific amino acid. Employing this idea, we may arbitrarily translate the sequence of amino acids in hemoglobin that differs in the three mutant forms into a corresponding nucleotide code as shown in Figure 80. The replacement of a single nucleotide with another within the critical trinucleotide sequence would give us the required change in code. (The reader will obviously not take all this too seriously. The most improbable hypotheses in science have turned out to be true, however, and this one certainly deserves some serious consideration for its novelty and coherence.)

One very interesting question is raised by the existence of three mutant forms of hemoglobin differing from one another in respect to a single "locus." Why, with some 300 amino acid residues in a hemoglobin monomer to choose from, has the accident of mutation occurred, and been perpetuated, in the same place three times? The phenomenon is qualitatively reminiscent of the results obtained by Benzer in his analysis of mutants in the rII region of bacteriophage T4 where he observed that, out of many hundreds of mutant colonies selected, a disproportionately great number involved mutation in the *same* genetic locus, whereas others were modified only rarely. The nonrandom distribution of affected loci, both in the bacteriophage case for which we have a good deal of genetic information, and for human hemoglobin for which we unfortunately have very little, might mean that only certain mutations are "permissible" and that the degree of permissibility is slight in most of the genetic material. We might equally well suggest, however, that some unsuspected peculiarities of DNA structure favor the modification of some lengths of nucleotide sequence more than others. Most probably, the mutant hemoglobin genes have been preserved because of the selective advantage they have conferred on the affected individuals. (Sickle-cell anemia, for example, is correlated with decreased susceptibility to clinical malaria.)

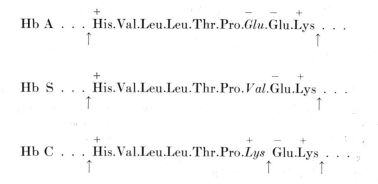

Figure 79. The differences in amino acid sequence between normal hemoglobin, sickle-cell hemoglobin and hemoglobin C. The arrows indicate the points of attack by trypsin which have lead to the production of the peptide fragments shown in the figure.

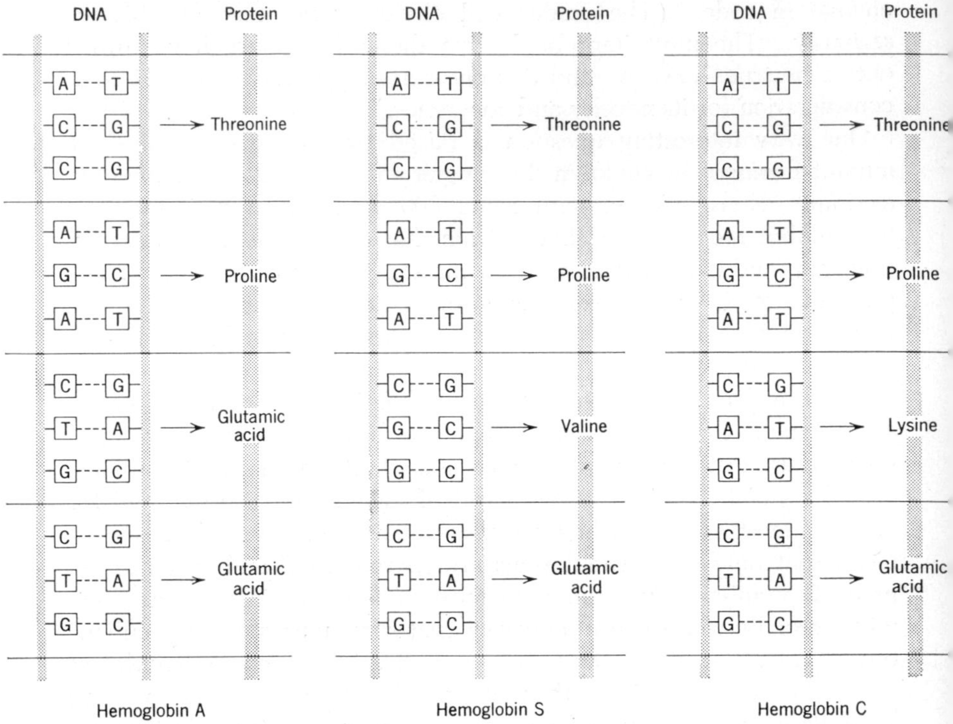

Figure 80. A hypothetical scheme showing how the structure of deoxyribonucleic acid might be related to the structures of hemoglobin A (normal hemoglobin), hemoglobin S (sickle-cell hemoglobin), and hemoglobin C. The diagram suggests a correspondence between triplets of purine and pyrimidine bases and individual amino acid residues. A change in the base sequence corresponding to the third amino acid from the top of the drawing could conceivably lead to the changes in code required for the modifications in sequence shown in Figure 79. The reader should be very much aware of the completely speculative nature of this diagram.

In the absence of further chemical data of the sort available for the human hemoglobins, it may be of value to examine in more detail some of the research now in progress which can be expected to settle some of the problems that we have posed. Many groups of investigators are busily engaged in attempts to isolate and characterize particular proteins from organisms that differ in genotype by a single mutation. We have already referred to the studies of Horowitz and Fling (Chapter 2) on the tyrosinases of *Neurospora* mutants in which differences in heat stability and activation energies of thermal inactivation were demonstrated. Rigid purification of these tyrosinases, and subsequent study of their chemical structure, may well lead to another situation like that of the hemoglobins for which the direct chemical consequences of mutation can be shown. Others of the protein systems under investigation, listed in Table 14, also promise to be extremely informative, particularly those involving easily isolated proteins like the β-lactoglobulins of milk. Because of their flexibility as regards genetic analysis, however, the bacteria and bacteriophages are, at present, receiving the most concerted attention. For example, no less than three laboratories are in the midst of the particular problem of determining the effects of mutation in the h region of bacteriophage T2 on the chemical nature of the phage particle.

The host range (h) region of the genetic material of bacteriophage T2 determines whether or not a phage particle will adsorb to a specific bacterial cell host. Thus the wild-type phage, T2h^+, will adsorb to and infect E. coli of the B strain but not of the B/2 strain, whereas h mutants will attack both B and B/2. Thus wild-type particles (h^+), when grown on a Petri dish containing agar in which is uniformly distributed a mixture of B and B/2 E. coli, will lyse only the B cells and a turbid plaque will be formed. On the other hand, h mutants will attack both B and B/2 and a completely clear plaque will result. (It is convenient, in what follows, to think of an h^+ mutation as a "defect" in the "normal" h region of the genetic strand.) This difference in phenotypic behavior can be made the basis for a quantitative estimate of the proportion of h and h^+ particles and has been applied by Streisinger and Franklin[4] for the location of various h mutants along the linear genetic map in a manner much like that employed by Benzer for the mapping of r mutants in bacteriophage T4.

Since use of the technique of fine-structure mapping in bacteriophage will become more and more common, it will be instructive to examine briefly the general approach to the mapping of the h region as an additional example.

An h-type phage arbitrarily named $h_0{}^0$, was plated on mixed B and B/2 cells as above described, and the turbid plaques were chosen as examples of reversions to the h^+ genotype. In this way there was obtained a series of mutants of the h^+ variety. Fourteen h^+ mutants having low reversion indices* were then crossed with each other as

* All the h^+ mutants were examined for their propensity to revert spontaneously to the h phenotype, and those having a high "reversion index" were discarded since such mutants would have introduced technical difficulties in subsequent studies of the ability of pairs of h^+ mutants to yield h phenotypes by genetic recombination.

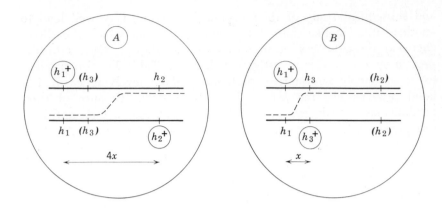

The "defective," h^+ loci are encircled. During the formation of progeny a process analogous to crossing over takes place. The probability that recombination of h_1 and h_2 will occur in the doubly infected cell, A, is four times greater than the probability that h_1 and h_3 will recombine in B.

The relative positions of h_1^+, h_2^+, and h_3^+ might then be

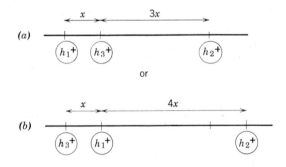

The correct order, $h_1^+-h_3^+-h_2^+$, may be established by crossing mutant h_2^+ with h_3^+. Recombination here will correspond to $3x$ rather than $5x$.

Figure 81. Establishing the relative separation and order of h^+ loci by two factor crosses.

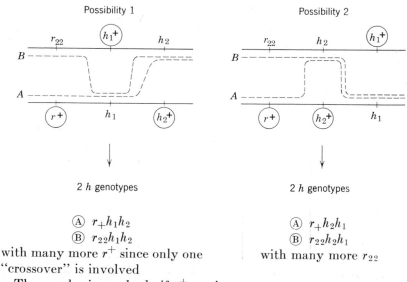

Possibility 1

r_{22} $(h_1{}^+)$ h_2

B

A

(r^+) h_1 $(h_2{}^+)$

↓

2 h genotypes

(A) $r_+h_1h_2$
(B) $r_{22}h_1h_2$

with many more r^+ since only one "crossover" is involved

Possibility 2

r_{22} h_2 $(h_1{}^+)$

B

A

(r^+) $(h_2{}^+)$ h_1

↓

2 h genotypes

(A) $r_+h_2h_1$
(B) $r_{22}h_2h_1$

with many more r_{22}

Thus, order is r_{22}–h_1–h_2 if r^+ are in excess,
or r_{22}–h_2–h_1 if r_{22} are in excess.

Figure 82. Establishing the absolute order of h^+ loci by three-factor crosses ($r_{22}h_1{}^+ \times r^+h_2{}^+$).

well as with the original h^+ strain by mixed infection of *E. coli* B. The progeny were examined (by the "turbid-or-clear" plaque test) for the relative proportion of h phenotypes that had formed through recombination (Figure 81). Each pair of h^+ mutants was found to yield h recombinants with a characteristic and reproducible frequency. All these frequencies were low, however (less than 1 per cent), indicating that the h^+ mutants examined all occurred within a region along the genetic map of less than two recombination units. (As discussed in Chapter 4, the total "length" of the genetic material in T2 phage may correspond to as much as 800 such units.)

Having established that all the various h^+ mutations occurred within a small region of the map, it was necessary to determine the order in which they were arranged with respect to one another. This was done through the use of three-factor crosses, a procedure with a forbidding name but one that is perfectly straightforward when thought of in terms of a simple model (Figure 82).

Crosses were made by mixed infection of strain B bacteria with bacteriophages containing, in addition to one of the h^+ loci, either the wild type, r^+, or the mutant, r_{22} (which belong to the so-called

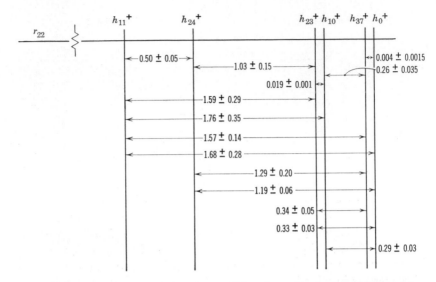

Figure 83. Genetic map of h^+ mutants. Taken from the studies of G. Streisinger and N. Franklin on the genetic determination of host range in bacteriophage T2, *Cold Spring Harbor Symposia Quant. Biology,* **21,** 103 (1956).

plaque-type mutants that were mapped by Benzer). The preparation of these doubly marked mutants requires a considerable amount of technical manipulation involving repeated back-crossing and selection and we shall not attempt to describe the details of the chore. Suffice it to say that strains of bacteriophage were obtained which permitted crosses of the type $r_{22}h_1{}^+h_2 \times r^+h_1h_2{}^+$ to be made, where the r_{22} locus is situated 24 recombination units from the h region as determined by two-factor crosses.

The relative location of two h^+ loci, $h_1{}^+$ and $h_2{}^+$, with respect to the r_{22} locus may be determined by the estimation of the proportion of the h mutants formed by recombination which is r^+ in character. The applicability of this test becomes clear upon inspection of the schematic representation shown in the figure. If the order of loci is r_{22}–h_1–h_2 rather than r_{22}–h_2–h_1, a far greater proportion of h-type recombinants will be r^+ since the incorporation of the segregated h alleles into one functional unit requires only one "crossover" in the first instance and two in the second. All of this deduction involves, of course, the assumptions we have mentioned earlier, including the reality of a linear arrangement of genetic loci in phage and the availability of a mechanism of crossover at least analogous to that generally invoked for recombination in the chromosomes of higher or-

THE MOLECULAR BASIS OF EVOLUTION

ganisms. These assumptions are, operationally speaking, applicable in the present case. The order of h^+ loci shown on the map in Figure 83, which were determined from the three-factor cross data, are compatible with the distances between the loci which was indicated by the preliminary two-factor cross experiments.

Before considering these genetic observations in terms of the hereditary control of phage chemistry, one further observation needs to be reviewed. This concerns the demonstration of the functional unity of the h region. Do all the h^+ mutations in the "map" shown in Figure 83 belong to a single unit of function (a "cistron"), or is it possible that they are divided into more than one group and act cooperatively in the determination of host range specificity? A decision may be made by use of the *cis-trans* test which we have previously described in relation to the r mutants. Streisinger[4] demonstrated that all the h mutants belong to a single functional unit by comparing the effectiveness of crosses of the *cis* type ($h \times h^+$) and of the *trans* type ($h_1^+ \times h_2^+$) in producing h phenotypes (i.e., phage which adsorbs to both B and B/2 bacteria). If, in Figure 84, each

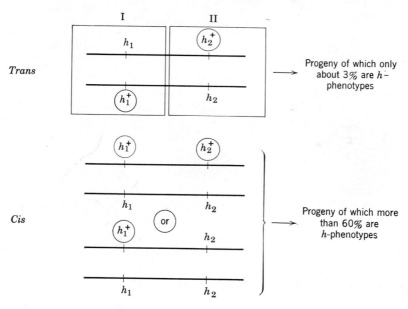

Figure 84. Application of the *cis-trans* test to determine the functional unity of the h region in the genetic material of bacteriophage T2. We may conclude that portions I and II of the h region of the hereditary material of bacteriophage T2 cannot act cooperatively to yield an "unblemished" h phenotype. The entire h region must be free of h^+ loci.

GENES AS DETERMINANTS OF PROTEIN STRUCTURE

of the indicated portions of the genetic strand acts separately, and they cooperatively produce a normal *h* phenotype, all the progeny in such a mixed infection should have the *h* character. It was found, however, that only a very small proportion of the progeny were *h* in phenotype (about 3 per cent, of the order of that to be expected from crossover and other sequelae of recombination). In the case of the *cis* arrangement (Figure 84), a high percentage of *h* pheno-

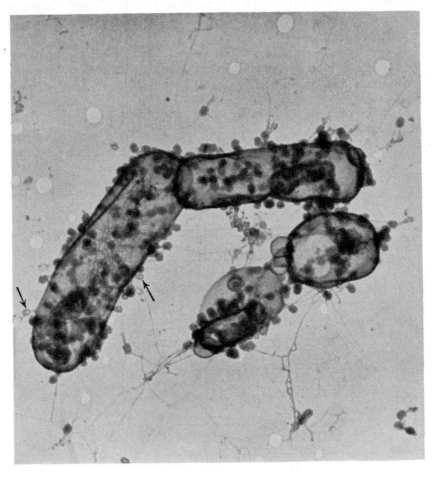

Figure 85. Electron photomicrograph of bacteriophage T2 adsorbed on cell walls of *E. coli* B. Some of the adsorbed virus particles have lost their DNA, presumably by injection into the bacterial cell (see arrows). This photograph was obtained through the kindness of Dr. Thomas F. Anderson of the Institute for Cancer Research, Philadelphia, Pa.

types was observed (about 60 per cent). (Enough phenotypically h material is presumably made by the all-h strand to confer this character on some of the h^+ genomes as well as the h. That is, genetically h^+ phage may have, associated with their protein coats, some h-type host-range protein). It may be concluded, therefore, that only a functionally complete h region will suffice for the expression of the h character.

We are now in a position to consider the genetic map of the h region in terms of what it does for the bacteriophage particle. Our attention must, of course, be directed at that part of the chemistry (and morphology) of T2 which has to do with its adsorption to host cells. Phage particles attach to bacterial cells by the tips of their tails (Figure 85). The same sort of attachment occurs with phage "ghosts" prepared by suddenly exposing intact phage to an osmotic shock. Since the phage ghost is essentially all protein, except for traces of carbohydrate present in such small amounts that its functional importance is fairly unlikely, it may be concluded that the business of attachment involves a specific protein component. Further support for the protein nature of the adsorbing substance comes from the fact that the kinetics of inactivation of the adsorptive capacity by agents like urea are very similar to those of protein denaturation. It has also been observed that the blocking of amino groups in phage prevents attachment to bacteria.

We may approach the problem of isolating and characterizing the protein component responsible for host range specificity in two ways. First, we may proceed to isolate various fragments from disrupted phage particles. Such studies have been carried out by S. Brenner and his colleagues in the Cavendish Laboratory at the University of Cambridge. These investigators have concluded that the host-range function is carried in the slender fibers that are attached to, and wrapped around, the tail of the virus particle (Figure 86) and have prepared highly purified concentrates of free fibers for chemical study.

A second approach to the problem involves the fractionation of the total protein mixture making up phage ghosts in the same way that we would approach the isolation of an enzyme from a crude tissue extract. Phage ghosts may be solubilized in a number of ways that should not cause modification in the covalent structure of the component proteins, and solutions prepared with such agents as urea and guanidine appear to be amenable to study by chromatographic, electrophoretic, and ultracentrifugal techniques. (See Figures 87 and 88, for example.)

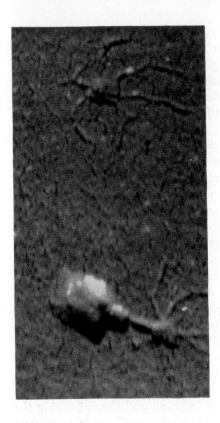

Figure 86. Electron photomicrograph of T2 bacteriophage, disrupted by treatment with N-ethyl maleimide. This photograph was obtained through the kindness of Mrs. E. R. Kaufman and Dr. A. M. Katz of the National Institutes of Health, Bethesda, Maryland.

Both the morphological and "chemical" attacks on the fractionation problem require a test for functional activity. Although not direct, a test has been devised based on the fact that the antigenicity of the T-even bacteriophages against rabbit antiphage antibody is controlled by the same genetic locus as that which determines the host range. Thus, Streisinger[5] has shown that no measurable recombination occurs between the determinants of host range and the determinants of serotype. (The reader must be asked to assume the validity of this conclusion; he may, however, wish to read the elegant paper of Streisinger,[5] in which the details and arguments are presented.) We may, then, hopefully assay any given protein fraction or morphological fraction for activity by estimating its ability to block the phage-neutralizing action of an inactivating antibody preparation.

The studies on the chemical consequences of mutation in the h region of bacteriophage have only just begun, and the problems of isolation must first be solved. It seems likely, however, that these investigations, as well as others concerned with other regions of the

THE MOLECULAR BASIS OF EVOLUTION

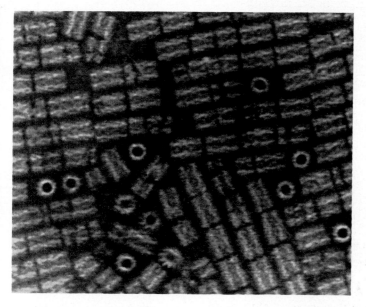

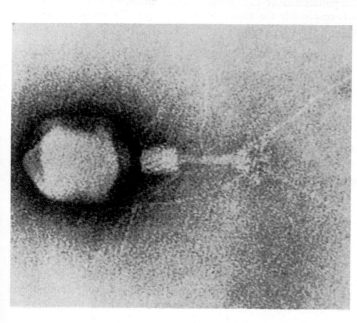

Figure 86 (continued). Left: Electronmicrograph of H_2O_2-treated bacteriophage T2 showing the head, core, contracted sheath, and tail fibers attached to the base of the core ($\times 300,000$). Right: Purified sheaths, some on end and some lying flat ($\times 300,000$). These photographs were obtained through the kindness of Dr. Sydney Brenner of the Cavendish Laboratory, University of Cambridge, England, who took these pictures together with his colleagues G. Streisinger, R. W. Horne, S. P. Champe, L. Barnett, and S. Benzer (*Journal of Molecular Biology*, 1959, in press). The preparations were made by the negative-staining technique described by S. Brenner and R. W. Horne (*Biochimica et Biophysica Acta*, 1959, in press).

GENES AS DETERMINANTS OF PROTEIN STRUCTURE

181

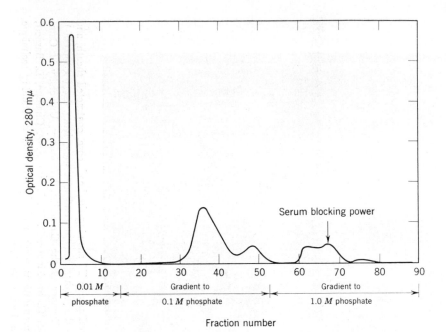

Figure 87. Partial purification of the protein component in ghosts of bacteriophage T2 which is responsible for serum blocking power (see text) and which presumably determines the host range of the phage. A preparation of "ghosts" was dissolved in ice-cold 5.2 M urea at pH 7.4 and chromatographed on a column of the cation exchanger XE-64. From W. J. Dreyer, A. Katz, and C. B. Anfinsen, *Federation Proc.*, **17**, 214 (1958).

genetic map of phage, should ultimately enable us to make direct point-by-point comparisons of genetic changes and structural modifications in protein molecules. The particular power of the bacteriophage approach, and of similar studies on other microbial systems,* is the extreme discrimination of the genetic mapping for these "or-

* For example, C. Levinthal and A. Garen, of the Massachusetts Institute of Technology, have recently begun the mapping of the "cistron" which controls the synthesis of an alkaline phosphatase in *E. coli*. This enzyme is synthesized in large quantities when phosphate is limiting in the culture medium. Organisms are grown on plates, containing medium or low phosphate concentration, which are then sprayed with nitrophenylphosphate. Alkaline phosphatase-containing cells cleave the phosphate ester to yield the yellow-colored nitrophenol. Bacterial colonies containing the enzyme thus become yellow, some mutants remain white, and certain mutants, having enzyme of intermediate activity, are weakly colored. The enzymes, active or inactive, may be isolated from the various strains and are at present being subjected to structural analysis.

ganisms." If Benzer's calculation of the length of the "recon" in terms of nucleotide units in the DNA chain proves to be reasonably correct, we may expect to be able to distinguish, genetically, between loci as closely packed as those determining the three hemoglobins investigated by Ingram. In the h region, for example, the locus $h_{37}{}^+$ appears to be only 0.004 recombination units from $h_0{}^+$. Translated into Benzer's nucleotide language, this distance would correspond to about the distance between one nucleotide pair. In spite of the wishful chemical thinking and genetic uncertainty involved in all these speculations, it must be very clear why the biochemist is willing to risk the gamble of time and effort required to test the gen-

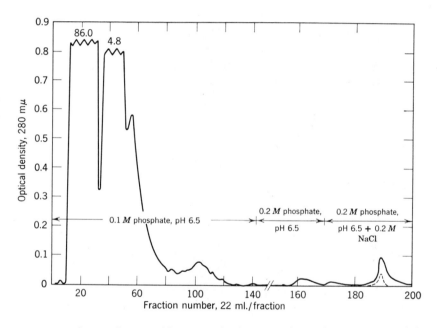

Figure 88. The purification of lysozyme from lysates of *E. coli* on a column of the cation exchanger, XE-64. The small chromatographic peak at the far right of the chromatogram contains the lysozyme activity (the dotted curve). Lysozyme may also be isolated from bacteriophage ghosts. The starting material of choice, however, is an *E. coli* lysate. Enough lysozyme is presumably synthesized following infection of *E. coli* cells with phage to more than satisfy the needs for the formation of progeny. The excess enzyme within the infected bacterial cells is then released into the surrounding culture medium upon lysis. The enzyme emerging from the ion exchange column is purified several thousandfold over its concentration in the crude lysate. From unpublished experiments of Dr. W. J. Dreyer, National Heart Institute, Bethesda, Maryland.

eral hypothesis. With luck, the answers might begin to clarify some of the most central problems of biology.

REFERENCES

1. L. Pauling, H. A. Itano, S. J. Sanger, and I. C. Wells, *Science,* **110,** 543 (1949).
2. H. Hörlein and G. Weber, *Deut. med. Wochschr.,* **73,** 876 (1948).
3. V. M. Ingram, *Nature,* **180,** 326 (1957).
4. G. Streisinger and N. C. Franklin, "Genetic Mechanisms: Structure and Function," *Cold Spring Harbor Symposia on Quant. Biol.,* **21,** 103 (1956).
5. G. Streisinger, *Virology,* **2,** 388 (1956).

chapter 9

ON THE ACCURACY

OF

PROTEIN SYNTHESIS

Except for the relatively minor influence of environmental factors, the phenotypic potentialities of an individual are determined by the genetic information in his chromosomes. In this book we have taken as a working hypothesis an even more specific proposition, namely, that the phenotypic picture presented by an organism is the summation of the effects, physical and catalytic, produced by the complement of protein molecules characterizing the species in question. That is to say, we assume that the genetic information available to an organism is first translated into protein structure, each gene determining specific details of a corresponding protein molecule, either alone or in collaboration with other genes. For example, we may think of the structure and physiological properties of hemoglobin as being determined by a single hemoglobin gene or "cistron" (see Chapter 4) or perhaps by several cooperating genes having to do with each of the peptide chains of hemoglobin and with the folding and cross attachments between them. The biosynthesis and arrangement of nonprotein substances such as carbohydrates and fats, and the distribution and integration of these secondary products into characteristic cellular systems, might then be considered to be the business of the proteins as agents of the genotype, acting as enzymes, hormones, and structural subunits of morphology.

Since we know that even a single gene mutation, causing a very limited change in the structure of a single protein species (e.g. the sickle-cell hemoglobin case discussed in the previous chapter), can induce a marked variation in phenotypic behavior, it becomes of prime importance in these considerations to examine the accuracy of the mechanisms by which proteins are synthesized and to try to appraise the degree to which errors in these mechanisms may occur. If a change in the structure of a protein involving a single amino acid residue can cause a marked change in function, we may justifiably be rather concerned by the influence of random heterogeneities in structure caused by biosynthetic errors. When we speak of the "control" of protein synthesis by genes, we would like to have some idea of the limits within which this control is exercised.

The highly developed techniques now available for the physicochemical study of proteins have made it possible to detect inhomogeneities in protein preparations caused by differences as small as the presence or absence of a single amide nitrogen group in a fraction of a population of molecules in solution. The apparent inhomogeneity of "pure" proteins may become even more marked as time goes on. In spite of such elegant tools as ion exchange chromatography, countercurrent distribution, and refined electrophoresis machines, we must recognize that the criteria of homogeneity are only relative and that heterogeneities not observable by presently available methods may, tomorrow, be detected on the basis of new, more discriminating procedures.

Since proteins are very complicated organic chemicals, they may naturally exist in a number of isomeric forms. We can conveniently classify such variations under two major headings, using terms suggested by D. Steinberg and E. Mihalyi in their recent review on protein chemistry.[1] Variations in the structure of a protein may be attributed to *sequential* or to *configurational* isomerism. The former classification refers to differences in amino acid sequence between individual molecules and, for convenience, is defined to include other aspects of structure which involve covalent bonds such as disulfide bridges, phosphate ester linkages, and amide nitrogen groups. These are the stable, black-or-white parameters of structure, not modified by the ordinary methods of handling proteins during purification and storage. Configurational isomerism, on the other hand, refers to differences in the mode of coiling of peptide chains or to the location, frequency, and stability of noncovalent bonds. Such isomerism is to be expected in aqueous solutions since the bonds responsible for the secondary and tertiary structure of proteins are strongly affected by the acidity, polarity, and temperature of the environment.

Colvin, Smith and Cook, in their review[2] written in 1954, have presented a list of examples from the literature in which inhomogeneity has been demonstrated in protein preparations, presumably of a high degree of purity. Thus, to quote only a few examples, lysozyme, ribonuclease, and ovalbumin showed reversible boundary spreading upon electrophoretic analysis, human gamma globulin appeared heterogeneous both by electrophoretic and by ultracentrifugal criteria, and insulin could be resolved into two components by countercurrent distribution techniques. These authors have chosen to interpret the experimental results in terms of a "microheterogeneity" in structure and suggest that "it seems more correct to describe a native protein, not in terms of a finite number of definite chemical entities, but as a population of closely related individuals which may differ either discretely or continuously in a number of properties." They have suggested that, should "microheterogeneity" be observed for all native proteins, the cellular mechanisms for the synthesis of proteins need not be specific and rigid, and that there might exist a broad spectrum of individual protein "subspecies" within any single "species," differing in enzymic, hormonal, or physicochemical properties. This conclusion was certainly an understandable one on the basis of the information available in 1954. It is now apparent, however, that many of the examples which supported the concept of "microheterogeneity" could be included in the list quoted only because of the inadequacy of the available knowledge about the chemistry of these proteins. In the case of beef pancreatic ribonuclease, for example, we can separate on proper chromatographic columns two major and two very minor components. A similar family of ribonucleases may be shown to be present in sheep pancreas.[3] These four components appear to be present normally in pancreas tissue since they may be separated both from purified, crystalline starting materials and from crude extracts of pancreas glands. Electrometric titrations on the two major components isolated from beef pancreas have suggested that they differ by a single carboxyl group (or conversely by a single amide nitrogen group). Rather than assume a broad microheterogeneity in the sense of a spectrum of related materials, we might equally well conclude that "ribonuclease" is *not* a statistical population of related proteins but rather a limited group of well-defined chemical entities.

The complete absence of sequential isomerism in any sample of protein can only be established by the *quantitative* recovery of *all* the fragments on which the sequence reconstruction is based. In practice the optimal situation has never been reached, and, for the proteins and polypeptides that have been studied in detail hitherto, sequential purity can only be inferred from the fact that aberrant sequences of amino acid residues, not fitting into the final reconstruction, have not been observed. In the studies of Sanger and his colleagues on the structure of insulin, for example, an enormous array of peptide fragments was examined, and none of these was found to be incompatible with the sequences of the two chains as they finally emerged. Such studies give strong presumptive evidence for the sequential purity of the starting material. In other work, such as that of Shepherd and his collaborators on the structure of ACTH,[4] and in the careful chromatographic separation of the enzymatically produced fragments of ribonuclease by C. H. W. Hirs, S. Moore, W. H. Stein and L. Bailey (Chapter 5), careful balance sheets of recoveries were kept, and for many portions of the over-all sequences recoveries were quantitative within the experimental error of determination. In the case of ACTH none of the fragments was isolated in less than 70 per cent yield, and total recovery, on the average, was 93 per cent of the total starting material. In those fragments recovered in yields less than quantitative it was shown, by paper chromatography, by terminal amino acid analysis, and by the presence of integral molar ratios of constituent amino acids, that sequential purity was extremely likely.

These examples illustrate two of the ways in which we may appraise the homogeneity of a protein; first, by an examination of the internal consistency between the sequences of a large number of small peptide fragments in terms of the final reconstructed sequence of the polypeptide chain representing the common denominator and, second, by a consideration of the completeness of recovery of these fragments. Both methods are as good as the accuracy of methods of detection or analysis available for peptides and give a lower limit for the degree of purity. Except for special sorts of inhomogeneity which we shall discuss more fully later, most proteins or polypeptides that have been examined will probably appear to be at least 90 per cent or more pure by these criteria. The last 5 to 10 per cent (or 3 to 5 per cent when analysis is done by careful ion exchange chromatography) remains an unknown quantity and might conceivably obscure the presence of small amounts of physically similar but structurally different protein material.

Another more worrisome factor in this regard has to do with the extent to which closely related proteins might be removed from the major fraction during isolation procedures. The purification of a protein such as hemoglobin presents no problem of this sort, since the starting material, washed red cells, contains only insignificant amounts of other proteins and the yield of hemoglobin can be made nearly quantitative by careful experimental manipulation. Most enzymes and hormones, however, must be concentrated many hundreds or even thousands of times from their initial *in vivo* state of purity. Modern purification procedures are tremendously discriminating. Under circumstances in which two forms of the same protein, differing only by a carboxylic acid group, may be separated, it is not unlikely that very minor variations in charge or polarity within a family may result in the complete separation of related molecules.

For these reasons we cannot be categorical about the absence of microheterogeneity, even in the sense in which this term was used by Colvin, Smith and Cook. There is, however, no evidence which *requires* that we take the "broad spectrum" point of view, and it would seem unnecessary at the present time to think of protein biosynthesis as an inaccurate or arbitrary process.

A more optimistic alternative may be given as an explanation for the bald fact that a well-defined sequential isomerism *does* occur in certain proteins. Isomerism, as observed for the β-lactoglobulins, hemoglobins, serum haptoglobin, etc., may be thought of as the reflection of heterozygosity in the corresponding genetic material. In those instances in which adequate genetic analyses have been carried out, the occurrence of more than one form of a single protein has been attributable to the presence of sets of allelic genes. In most cases only two forms are observed. We do not find, for example, more than one abnormal hemoglobin in any one individual (except for varying amounts of the fetal form which many believe to be extremely similar or identical with a portion of adult homoglobin). On the other hand, multiple forms of certain other proteins have been observed in some instances. Proteins in the β-globulin fraction of the serum of cattle, for example, may be divided, by the sensitive starch gel electrophoresis method of O. Smithies,[5] into four or five well-separated subcomponents. It is important to emphasize, however, that these are *separable* and that what is obtained is not a smear of overlapping substances but rather a well-defined and reproducible pattern. By some techniques such as gradual salting-out precipitation, even highly purified human hemoglobin from normal individuals appears to be subdivisible into several components as observed by Roche and his colleagues.[6] Although most workers in the field consider this phenomenon to be due to artifacts introduced by interactions with salts and buffer molecules, it is still quite possible that the effect is a real one, one that is simply not demonstrable by the usual electrophoretic analysis employed for the study of the hemoglobin series.

We have discussed, in a previous chapter, the concept of genetic fine structure which suggests that each "gene" may be composed of a large number of subgenic chemical units, each contributing a small piece of information to the protein biosynthetic process. The occurrence of many abnormal forms of a protein in addition to the normal one cannot be excluded if this concept is generally applicable. Thus, the portion of the genetic material that has to do with a particular protein molecule might involve more than one "cistron." The synthesis of separate chains, or even of parts of the same chain of a protein, might be controlled by different genetic functional units. If this were the case, and if the mutations were not lethal ones and still permitted the synthesis of a functionally adequate protein, we can easily see that a multiplicity of closely related proteins could result through the cooperation of the several cistrons involved. The hemoglobins that have so far been separated and studied have differed in electric charge. Since electrophoresis would not distinguish between two hemoglobins differing, let us say, by the substitution of valine for isoleucine or of serine for threonine, other techniques for fractionation will be required to test this possibility.

The Significance of Amino Acid Analogue Incorporation

A large number of structural analogues of amino acids have been synthesized (Figure 89) and tested for their utilizability in protein biosynthesis. These include the methionine analogues, selenomethionine and ethionine, the phenylalanine analogues, o- and p-fluoro phenylalanine and β-2-thienylalanine, and the tryptophane analogue, 7-azatryptophane. They may be synthesized in radioactive form and thus furnish a powerful and sensitive tool for testing whether the mechanisms of protein biosynthesis are absolutely precise and specific or whether alternative structures may be formed by replacement of natural amino acid residues with man-made substitutes.

The results of such tests are clear-cut. Abnormal amino acids *can* be used. Cowie and Cohen,[7] for example, have grown a methionine-requiring mutant of *E. coli* in a medium completely free of methionine but containing selenomethionine instead. The cells were able to synthesize certain enzymes in a relatively normal manner in spite of the unusual nutritional circumstance, and the proteins of the daughter cells were of the selenomethionine variety. In another similar study, M. Gross and H. Tarver have shown that the proteins of *Tetrahymena pyriformis* can incorporate C^{14}-labeled ethionine. The incorporation represents true peptide bond formation since it was found that ethionine-containing peptides could be isolated from partial acid hydrolysates. An interesting experiment on analogue incorporation has been carried out by D. Steinberg and M. Vaughan, who studied the *in vitro* uptake of tritium-labeled *o*-fluorophenylalanine (see Figure 89) into the proteins of the minced hen's oviduct.[8] Pure lysozyme was then isolated from the tissue and digested with trypsin and chymotrypsin. The digest was subjected to fingerprinting as described in Chapter 7, and the peptides thus separated were analyzed for the presence of aromatic amino acids. A small proportion of the peptides that normally contained phenylalanine were found to contain the radioactive analogue in place of the natural amino acid.

Although analogues may be incorporated into proteins, the compromise with normalcy does not seem to be a happy one, for most of them also cause marked inhibition of growth. We can say nothing at the moment about the mechanism of this inhibition. Studies are now in progress in several laboratories to determine the efficiency of incorporation of analogues as a function of their degree of dissimilarity from the natural amino acid they mimic.

Nature appears to have been extremely clever in her choice of standard amino acids and has managed to choose some twenty which differ sufficiently to preclude mistakes in recognition. Valine and isoleucine residues are extremely similar from the point of view of three-dimensional structure, and it would not be too surprising to find an occasional lapse in the precision of protein assembly at points of protein structure involving one or the other of these amino acids. To my knowledge, however (within the limits of analytical accuracy mentioned earlier in this chapter), valine-isoleucine interchange has not been observed, except in samples of the same protein or polypeptide isolated from two different species or from an individual who is "heterozygous" for the material in question. On the other hand, D. Cowie and his colleagues have recently shown that a considerable amount of the methionine in *E. coli* proteins may be replaced by

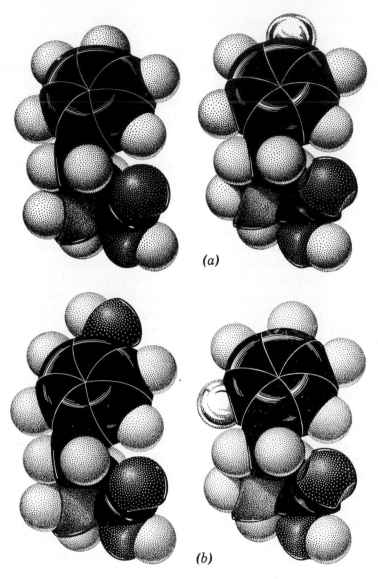

(a)

(b)

Figure 89. The molecular structure of some amino acids and amino acid analogues. (*a*) Phenylalanine and *p*-fluorophenylalanine, (*b*) tyrosine and *o*-fluorophenylalanine, (*c*) norleucine and methionine, (*d*) isoleucine and leucine. Al-

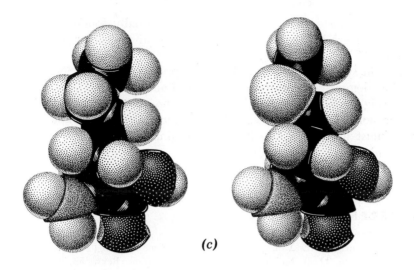

(c)

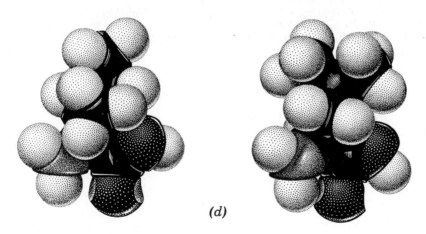

(d)

though norleucine is a chemical isomer of leucine and isoleucine, its molecular shape is much more similar to that of the sulfur-containing amino acid methionine than to that of isoleucine or leucine.

norleucine,[9] an amino acid which is not normally found in proteins but which exhibits a remarkable similarity in molecular appearance (Figure 89) to methionine.

Protein synthesis is not an absolutely precise process. Some amino acid analogues *can* substitute for natural amino acids. Nevertheless, the weight of evidence indicates that no mistakes are detectable under normal circumstances and that the protein assemble mechanism must have built into it an extraordinary capacity for structural discrimination.

REFERENCES

1. D. Steinberg and E. Mihalyi, *Ann. Rev. Biochem.*, **26**, 373 (1957).
2. J. R. Colvin, D. B. Smith, and W. H. Cook, *Chem. Revs.*, **54**, 687 (1954).
3. S. Äqvist and C. B. Anfinsen, *J. Biol. Chem.*, **234**, No. 5 (1959); C. B. Anfinsen, S. Äqvist, J. Cooke, and B. Jönsson, *J. Biol. Chem.*, **234**, No. 5 (1959).
4. R. G. Shepherd, S. D. Wilson, K. S. Howard, P. H. Bell, D. S. Davies, S. B. Davis, E. A. Eigner, and N. E. Shakespeare, *J. Am. Chem. Soc.*, **78**, 5067 (1956).
5. O. Smithies, *Biochem. J.*, **61**, 629 (1955).
6. J. Roche, Y. Derrien, and M. Roques, *Bull. soc. chim. biol.*, **35**, 933 (1953).
7. D. B. Cowie and G. N. Cohen, *Biochim. et Biophys. Acta*, **26**, 252 (1957).
8. I am grateful to Dr. Daniel Steinberg and Dr. Martha Vaughan of the National Heart Institute, Bethesda, Md., for information on these studies prior to publication.
9. Personal communication from Dr. D. B. Cowie of the Carnegie Institution, Department of Terrestrial Magnetism, Washington, D. C.

chapter 10

THE BIOSYNTHESIS
OF PROTEINS

There can be little doubt that the specific informa-
tion necessary for the biosynthesis of proteins is, in some way, woven
into the structure of the deoxyribonucleic acids of the chromosome.
Ample support for this conclusion is given by the numerous observations that have related Mendelian genes to individual protein molecules. As we have seen, the most direct evidence has come from instances in which the genetic results could be compared with the
chemical and physical properties of isolated, homogeneous proteins,
such as hemoglobin, tyrosinase, and β-lactoglobulin. Equally convincing are the results obtained by bacteriologists and virologists who
have demonstrated that highly purified samples of DNA are capable
of modifying both the genotype and phenotype of recipient cells, or
of inducing the formation of the relatively complicated protein complex which characterizes the bacteriophage particle.

It is clear, however, that protein synthesis can take place outside
the nucleus itself. In the reticulocyte, for example, hemoglobin synthesis proceeds at a rapid rate, and not until the cell has become a
mature erythrocyte does such synthesis cease. Similarly, in the alga
Acetabularia mediterranea, whose cell may be separated into nuclear

and anuclear halves, the latter fragment temporarily synthesizes protein at a rate even more rapid than that of the intact cell, although this synthetic activity soon disappears. If the biosynthesis of a specific, chemically definable protein like hemoglobin can continue in the absence of an intact nucleus, it becomes essential to focus our attention on the mechanism by which the requisite information might be transferred to, and perhaps temporarily stored in, the cytoplasm of cells.

The biosynthesis of protein is among the biological phenomena that are highly dependent on structural organization. Even when synthesis can proceed in the absence of a nucleus, the process is only temporarily maintained (although admittedly this degeneration might be due to deficiencies in any one of a number of metabolic factors only indirectly related to protein synthesis per se). Because of this dependence on structural integrity, the recent investigations of the nature of cellular substructure have contributed perhaps the most important advance toward an ultimate understanding of the nature of the biosynthetic mechanism. These studies, in spite of their emphasis on static morphology, are beginning to give us a picture of the cell as a highly organized system of interconnected metabolic units into which all the dramatic observations of the enzyme chemist and the geneticist must ultimately be fitted.

Two relatively new techniques—electron microscopy of ultrathin sections and differential sedimentation of cellular components in sucrose solutions—have been of particular importance in this process of the description of cellular architecture. The latter of these methods permits the isolation of more or less homogeneous samples of mitochondria, microsomes, nuclei, and other cell inclusions, allowing the study of the relative abilities of these particulate fractions to incorporate labeled precursors into nucleic acids and proteins. We shall discuss these observations later, but first let us look at some of the results, obtained through electron microscopy, which indicate how these functional components are arranged within the intact cell.

The electron micrograph in Figure 90, taken by Dr. George Palade of the Rockefeller Institute, is of guinea pig pancreas. Careful examination and measurement of many such photographs have established the presence in the cytoplasm of concentrically arranged membranes, having a thickness of about 40 A. These membranes, variously called the "endoplasmic reticulum," the "ergastoplasm," or simply the "intracellular cytoplasmic membrane," are studded throughout with small electron-dense granules. These are the gran-

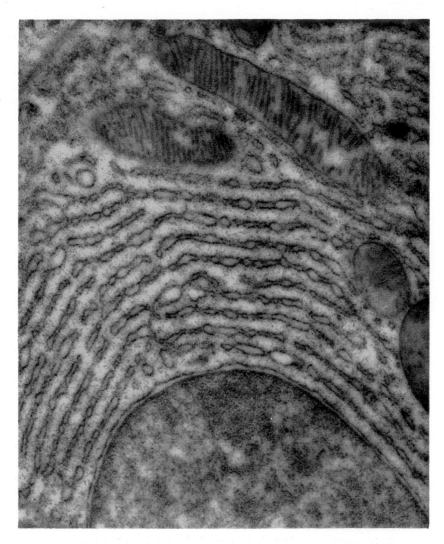

Figure 90. Electron photomicrograph of a section through a cell from the pancreas of the guinea pig. Magnification, 56,000×. The layered structures at the center of the photograph are the "endoplasmic reticulum" and consist of lipoidal membranes studded with particles rich in RNA. The oval, cross-channeled structures at the top are mitochondria. A portion of the cell nucleus is visible at the bottom of the photograph. This photograph was obtained through the kindness of Dr. George Palade of the Rockefeller Institute for Medical Research. From "The Endoplasmic Reticulum," *J. Biophys. Biochem. Cytology,* **2,** (suppl.) 85 (1956).

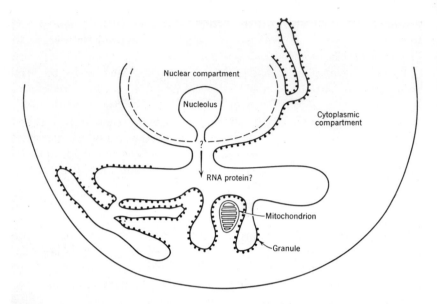

Figure 91. A schematic diagram of how some of the structural elements within a cell might be organized. The cytoplasm of the cell is visualized as being divided into two portions by the folded and invaginated endoplasmic reticulum, the "internal" portion being continuous with the outer surface of the nucleus and possibly directly connected with the nucleolus through a small channel. The "external" portion of the cytoplasm occupies a space between the endoplasmic reticulum and the plasma membrane of the cell and contains the mitochondria.

ules which, following homogenization of a tissue, may be isolated as a discrete fraction by differential centrifugation, attached to pieces of fragmented membrane. Sjöstrand and Hanzon[1] have reported that, in their experience (and this is generally confirmed by many investigators), the granule-studded membranes are always arranged so that they face the mitochondria, the cell membrane, or each other with their rough side, but that around the nucleus the smooth side of the membrane is presented. Such an arrangement would be compatible with the situation outlined schematically in Figure 91. Here the reticulum is visualized not as a number of independent membranes but as a large balloon-like structure surrounding the nucleus and crumpled upon itself. This would lead to the sort of orientation of granules suggested by Sjöstrand and Hanzon and would serve to divide the cell up into two major compartments, one containing the nucleus and the other the mitochondria, together with the cytoplasmic fluid in which they are bathed. Thus, the "crumpled balloon"

THE MOLECULAR BASIS OF EVOLUTION

arrangement would furnish the cell with a large surface as a site for metabolic activity and would also serve as a natural divider of the "genetic" and "assembly line" portions of the cell.

It must be emphasized that the scheme presented in Figure 91 is only the distillation of several possibilities considered reasonable by expert cytologists. It is included here only to indicate to the reader the degree of sophistication that has been reached in the study of cellular substructure. Uniformity of interpretation by experts is more than can be expected in any rapidly advancing field, and it is gratifying that most of the differences of opinion among cytologists revolve around relatively minor points.

When a tissue is homogenized, the endoplasmic reticulum is disintegrated. From recent analyses it would appear that the so-called microsome fraction is composed mainly of granules to which pieces of reticulum still adhere. Thus, treatment of microsomal preparations with lipoprotein-disrupting agents such as deoxycholate yields particles containing most of the RNA of the original preparation but only a small proportion (about one-sixth) of the original protein. With ribonuclease, on the other hand, which digests and depolymerizes the RNA, only membranous material is observed upon electron microscopic examination. In some tissues, like the hen's oviduct, the ergastoplasm is not as friable, and, even after fairly vigorous homogenization, a relatively intact membrane particle complex may be isolated by centrifugation at relatively low speeds.

The origin of the ergastoplasm is not established. It has recently been shown that, in the hepatic cells of animals fed after a prolonged fasting period, regeneration of membranes begins near the periphery of the cell. These membranes are free of granules and only later assume the studded appearance which characterizes them in an actively secreting cell. It has been suggested that the reticulum might be the product of the continuing process of pinocytosis (water imbibition) and phagocytosis (particle imbibition) at the cell surface. Electron microscope studies have indicated that engulfed fluids and solids are surrounded with a sheath of the external plasma membrane of the cell, pinched off during the passage of nutrients across the cell surface. This membrane ultimately becomes continuous with the endoplasmic reticulum. The observations, if substantiated, would require some rather vigorous metabolism. For example, as Swerdlow, Dalton, and Birks[2] have recently pointed out, if the incorporation of the plasma membrane into actively imbibing cells like macrophages were continuous, the cells would soon consist of nothing else. Such cells would obviously require active processes both for the regeneration of new plasma membrane and for the breakdown of reticulum as it accumulated and pressed in on the nucleus.

Cytological Aspects of Protein Synthesis

In 1940, T. Caspersson[3] suggested a general theory of protein bio-synthesis which is, in essence, still in accordance with observation. In his theory the genetic information within the DNA of the nucleus was pictured as being transmitted to the nucleolus through the medium of basic nucleohistones, rich in arginine and lysine. The nucleolus then converted this information into ribonucleoprotein which, in turn, induced and directed the biosynthesis of proteins by enzyme systems in the cytoplasm.

One aspect of this theory can probably be safely discarded. The role postulated for the nucleohistones was one of precursor for the purines and pyrimidines of the ribonucleoprotein. We now know, from isotope studies, that the building blocks of RNA are simple substances such as glycine, formate, and carbon dioxide and are not basic amino acids. We cannot, however, rule out the possibility that nucleohistones might serve as agents of information transfer, acting, in a sense, as negative prints of the specifically arranged nucleotide sequences of DNA.

In this connection, Wilkins and his colleagues have suggested the interesting hypothesis that protamines and nucleohistones might be wrapped around the double helix of the DNA strand (shown in profile in Figure 92). This suggestion, admittedly based on very preliminary X-ray studies, is consistent with certain amino acid se-quence data by Felix, Fischer, and Krekels.[4] About one-third of the residues in protamines are nonbasic, and these residues would have to occur at folds in the polypeptide chain to permit all basic side chains to associate with phosphate groups. The sequence analyses do in fact show that nonbasic residues occur in pairs and that folds such as those indicated in the figure would thus be possible.

What evidence can we marshal for the second step in Caspersson's theory, namely, that the nucleolus is concerned with the synthesis of cytoplasmic ribonucleoprotein? Here we find ourselves immersed in a mass of data, much of it conflicting. The fact, for example, that some enucleated cells can continue to form protein suggests that cytoplasm is autonomous in this respect. On the other hand, we may postulate that ribonucleoprotein, produced in the nucleus and containing genetic information, has a certain "life expectancy" in the

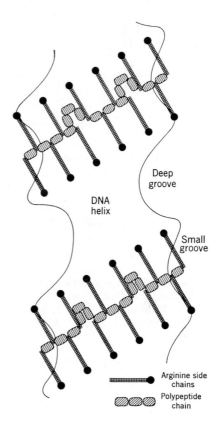

Figure 92. A diagram showing how protamine might be wrapped in a spiral fashion around the DNA double helix. The polypeptide chain is wound around the small groove of the helix. Phosphate groups of the DNA coincide with the basic ends of the arginine chains (black circles) of the protamine molecule. Non-basic residues are shown in pairs at the folds in the polypeptide chain. From M. H. F. Wilkins, *Cold Spring Harbor Symposia Quant. Biol.*, **21**, 75 (1956).

cell which varies from species to species, and that protein synthesis may proceed as long as some of this material remains functional.

Two types of experimental observation have a direct bearing on this question. The first, involving the measurement of rates of incorporation of various nucleic acid and protein precursors into the ribonucleoproteins of nucleus and cytoplasm, indicates that such substances are subject to a much greater metabolic flux in the former cellular compartment. As shown in Figure 93, nuclear RNA attains a much higher specific radioactivity than does cytoplasmic RNA when an animal is administered radioactive phosphate. Further, the peak of radioactivity is attained much more rapidly in the nuclear material. Thus, although the amount of RNA in the nucleolus is generally relatively small in comparison with that in the cytoplasm, the rate of turnover of the former is such that it might serve as a precursor of at least part of the cytoplasmic RNA.

A second type of approach has been made by Ficq and her col-

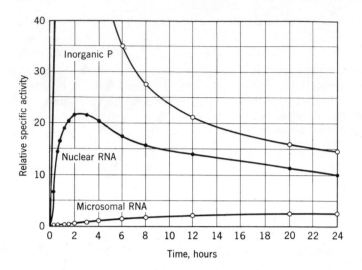

Figure 93. Relative specific activities of inorganic phosphate, nuclear RNA, and microsomal RNA of mouse liver tissue at various times after the administration of P^{32}. Redrawn from R. M. S. Smellie, *The Nucleic Acids*, volume 2 (E. Chargaff and J. N. Davidson, editors), Academic Press, 1955.

leagues,[5] using autoradiographic methods. After administration of radioactive glycine to rats and to starfish oöcytes, she observed that the rate of labeling of nuclear proteins was considerably higher than that for cytoplasmic proteins. In the starfish oöcyte the well-defined nucleolus showed particularly marked activity. Much of this radioactivity is rapidly washed out of nuclei when they are isolated from homogenized tissues.

These observations are consistent with the idea that cytoplasmic ribonucleoprotein stems from the nucleus. As usual, however, there is another side to the coin. Brachet and Szafarz have shown, for example, that cytoplasmic RNA of *Acetabularia* continues to incorporate the purine precursor, orotic acid, in spite of previous enucleation.[5] Further, Moldave and Heidelberger[6] have found that the ribonucleic acids of the nuclei, microsomes, and mitochondria show different chemical properties, such as variations in the ratios of heterocyclic bases and in nucleotide sequences. We are obviously far from an answer to the question of the essentiality of direct nuclear control of protein synthesis. Whether the present confusion is attributable to the presence of two distinct types of protein synthesis, one nuclear and one cytoplasmic, as has been suggested by Brachet and others, or whether experimental inconsistencies are due to the occurrence of

THE MOLECULAR BASIS OF EVOLUTION

processes in enucleated and otherwise disturbed cells that represent the dying gasps of a partially functional but abnormal mechanism, is a source of some of the more exciting speculations in the field.

Some very recent work does seem to offer strong support for the latter alternative. Stich and Plaut have examined the potentials for growth, protein synthesis, and differentiation of nuclear and anuclear halves of *Acetabularia* after exposure to ribonuclease action. Their results, summarized in Figure 94, show that, in the absence of a nucleus, normal growth and synthesis cannot be resumed after RNA degradation. Stich and Plaut suggest that the nuclear product which effects the recovery of nucleated halves is RNA, but they emphasize that this suggestion should not be extended to include *all* the cytoplasmic RNA but may apply only to a small and highly critical fraction produced by the nucleus. With this reservation, these observations are in good agreement with the results of Moldave and

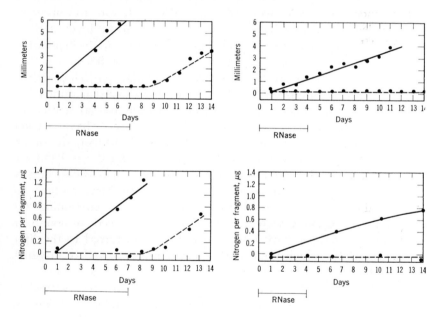

Figure 94. The effect of ribonuclease action on the growth and protein synthesis of nucleated and enucleated cell fragments of *Acetabularia mediterranea*. The top curves (left, nucleated; right, enucleated) show the effects of ribonuclease on growth and the bottom curves those on protein synthesis. Fragments were transferred to normal medium at the times indicated by the bars at the bottom of each graph. In the absence of a nucleus, normal growth and synthesis could not be resumed after RNA degradation. From H. Stich and W. Plaut, *J. Biophys. Biochem. Cytology*, **4**, 119 (1958).

THE BIOSYNTHESIS OF PROTEINS

Heidelberger already mentioned and also with studies recently reported by McMaster-Kaye and Taylor,[7] who show that what has hitherto been referred to as "nuclear" RNA may be divided into nucleolar and chromosomal fractions, only the former of which has an especially dynamic metabolism. It would begin to seem that the nucleolus may, as Caspersson suggested, occupy a very central position in the over-all process of protein biosynthesis.

The third step in Caspersson's scheme involves the production of cytoplasmic proteins by a process dependent on the ribonucleoproteins, whose possible origin we have just discussed. Here we seem to be on reasonably firm ground, at least from the biochemical point of view. It has long been known that the rate at which a tissue can synthesize protein is correlated with its RNA content. Studies with the ultraviolet microscope and with conventional staining methods demonstrated, rather early, that such actively proliferating tissues as root tips and yeast cells and such secretory cells as the exocrine cells of the pancreas and liver were all rich in RNA. It was also observed that enucleation of amoebae caused a rapid fall in the level of RNA, paralleled by a fall in the rate of labeled amino acid incorporation.

The most direct evidence for the essential role of RNA in protein synthesis comes from studies on isolated cellular particles. When the tissues of an animal which has been administered a radioactive amino acid are homogenized and subjected to differential sedimentation, it is found that the proteins of the microsomes have become most rapidly labeled. (We must keep in mind, however, the observations of Ficq on the extractability of protein from the isolated nucleus when appraising data obtained on isolated cell particles in general.) Subdivision of microsomal matter into arbitrary fractions by differential extraction showed that those fractions containing the highest levels of RNA were also most rapidly labeled, although, in later samples, radioactivity had been rapidly transferred to the lipoprotein matrix to which the ribonucleoprotein is attached or in which it is dissolved.

The endoplasmic reticulum disappears during mitosis, as well as during starvation, as we have discussed earlier, and it is of interest in connection with Caspersson's general hypothesis that this behavior is shared by the nucleolus, which we have indicated might be implicated as a central site of ribonucleoprotein synthesis. The parallel disappearance and reappearance of ribonucleoprotein-rich reticulum on the one hand, and of the ribonucleoprotein-producing nucleolus on the other, furnish inferential evidence for the idea that these two

THE MOLECULAR BASIS OF EVOLUTION

cellular components are somehow linked in the process of establishing information-rich biosynthetic machinery in the cytoplasm.

Protein Synthesis in Ruptured-Cell Preparations[8]

Tissue homogenates, although they incorporate amino acids only weakly and lack the integrated information system of the cell, have the advantage that the need for certain essential cell components becomes emphasized. Various cofactors or substrates may then be screened for their capacity to stimulate the synthesis of proteins.

It was observed, in a number of preliminary studies, that homogenates could support the incorporation of labeled amino acids into proteins when ATP was added as an energy source. Mitochondria, which serve as the site of ATP production through oxidative phosphorylation, could substitute for added ATP in large part. The incorporated amino acids in such systems are found mainly in the microsome fraction of the homogenate (although mitochondria would also appear to support the synthesis of some proteins, e.g. cytochrome c).

A major contribution was made by P. C. Zamecnik and E. B. Keller[9] when they observed that, if more gentle homogenizing techniques were employed, a reconstructed system consisting of microsomes and a particle-free supernatant would incorporate labeled precursors when supplied with an energy source such as phosphocreatine or phosphoenolypyruvate. This incorporation was specific for the natural L-amino acids and was abolished by the addition of ribonuclease. The true synthesis of peptide bonds was demonstrated by the isolation of peptides from partial hydrolysates of the protein which contained C^{14}.

Pursuing the dissection of this system, Zamecnik[8] and his colleagues found that a protein fraction could be prepared from the supernatant by precipitation at pH 5. This fraction no longer contained bound nucleotides, which were present in the original crude extract, and could support amino acid incorporation only when ATP and either guanosine triphosphate or guanosine diphosphate were added.

It was suggested by F. Lipmann[8] in 1941 that amino acids might be raised to an energy level, sufficient to permit them to undergo peptide bond condensations, by conjugation with high-energy phosphate groups. Support for this prediction was obtained by M. Hoagland and others,

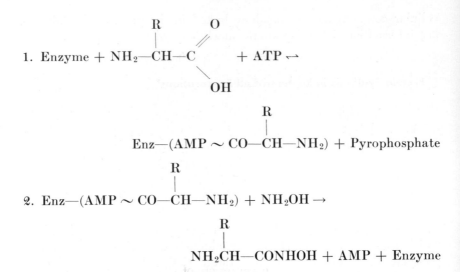

1. Enzyme + $NH_2-CH(R)-C(=O)OH$ + ATP →

   Enz—(AMP ~ CO—CH(R)—NH$_2$) + Pyrophosphate

2. Enz—(AMP ~ CO—CH(R)—NH$_2$) + NH$_2$OH →

   NH$_2$CH(R)—CONHOH + AMP + Enzyme

Figure 95. A postulated mechanism for the activation of amino acids for protein synthesis. In step 1 the amino acid is converted to an enzyme-bound acyl phosphate derivative of adenylic acid (AMP). This complex may be utilized for intracellular protein synthesis or, as shown in the figure, may be reacted with hydroxylamine to yield the amino acid hydroxamate.

who showed that during the incubation of amino acids with ATP and an enzyme fraction prepared from the "pH 5 enzyme" derivatives were formed which had the characteristics of an active acyl compound; that is, they formed hydroxamates upon treatment with hydroxylamine.[8] Although the active intermediate compounds have not been isolated in more than trace amounts, the fact that hydroxamates are formed and that pyrophosphate is liberated during the reaction strongly suggests that the chemical events may be described by the formulas in Figure 95. Several investigators have recently synthesized the postulated amino acid adenylates and report that they can undergo *nonspecific* condensations with pre-existing free amino groups in proteins. The decision whether AMP-amino acid conjugates are real, or only apparent, participants in the pathway between free amino acid and protein must therefore depend on future research. The postulated reactions are appealing because of their analogy to already proven activation reactions for other substrate molecules, such as fatty acids. They are also an attractive possibility for the simple reason that enzymes which form amino acid adenylates *do* exist in the cytoplasm of cells.

THE MOLECULAR BASIS OF EVOLUTION

The Question of Intermediates in Protein Biosynthesis

Perhaps the greatest puzzle in protein biosynthesis is the question of how sequences are determined and how cross-linking and folding of peptide chains is brought about in a way that yields biologically specific proteins. It seems likely that much of this process must involve RNA, since this is the only obvious substance in the cytoplasm which bears some structural (and probably metabolic) relationship to the DNA of the nucleus, from which most of or all the information that specifies the patterns of the protein molecules must originally stem. Indeed, a number of investigators have recently obtained suggestive evidence for the involvement of a soluble, non-microsomal, RNA fraction of the cytoplasm which is extremely active in incorporating labeled amino acids and which may act as an intermediate transport system between activated amino acids and the ribonucleoproteins of the endoplasmic reticulum.*

If we assume that RNA serves as some sort of "template" for the assembly of proteins, must there be a separate ribonucleoprotein "template" for each cellular protein, or is it possible that there exists some facet in protein synthesis which permits the utilization of common information for the synthesis of many different kinds of protein molecules? The evidence we have for the presence of repeating patterns in protein biosynthesis is, at present, very meager but suggestive enough to make the idea worthy of serious consideration. Several groups of investigators have gone to considerable trouble in assembling the known amino acid sequences in proteins (making up a total of some 400 or 500 residues) and subjecting their sequential arrangement to a rough statistical analysis for the occurrence of "repeats." As yet, no definite pattern has emerged from such efforts, although certain special sequences are found with surprising frequency. The dipeptide sequence, Ser.Arg, for example, has been demonstrated in ribonuclease, chymotrypsin, lysozyme, salmine (twice), and phosphorylase (and this statement is based on only a cursory search of the literature on protein structure). The phosphoproteins so far examined involve phosphoserine-containing sequences with remarkable similarity in structure. Table 16 contains a list of some of these, derived from proteins with no obvious connection except, perhaps, the fact that they are all secretory proteins. In every

* Several articles on the chemical nature of intermediates in protein synthesis and on the kinetics of the assembly of proteins are listed at the end of this chapter.[11, 12, 13, 14] These aspects of protein biosynthesis are under active study in many laboratories, but the field is still too confused for constructive discussion.

case the phosphoserine residue is either preceded or followed by a dicarboxyic amino acid.

Even more striking is the similarity in the sequence of amino acids associated with the "active centers" of a number of enzymes. A large number of enzymes have been found to be sensitive to reagents of the sort typified by the compound, di-isopropylfluorophosphate (DFP). Such reagents presumably inactivate by reacting with spe-

TABLE 16

Amino Acid Sequences Containing O-Phosphorylserine (SerP)[a]

Pepsin	Thr.SerP.Glu
Egg albumin	Glu.SerP.Ala
	Asp.SerP.Glu.Ileu.Ala
α-Casein	SerP.Glu
	SerP.Ala
	Glu.SerP

[a] A general discussion of phosphorus-containing proteins is given by G. Perlmann, *Advances in Protein Chemistry*, volume 10, (M. L. Anson, K. Bailey, and J. T. Edsall, editors), Academic Press, 1955.

cific serine hydroxyl groups to yield the O-di-isopropyl phosphate derivative (DIP protein). After partial hydrolysis of DIP proteins, the acidic phosphopeptides may be isolated and characterized. Four enzymes, trypsin, chymotrypsin, phosphoglucomutase, and thrombin, have been studied in particular detail in relation to the DFP reaction, and it has been found that the amino acid sequence in the neighborhood of the tagged serine residue is probably identical in all four cases.[10] Although the complete sequence has been established unequivocally for only two of the proteins, it is almost certain from the preliminary data that all four involve the sequence

Gly.Asp.SerP.Gly.Glu.Ala

in which the phosphate group is derived from the phosphorylating reagent except in the case of phosphoglucomutase, which contains phosphate as an integral part of the enzyme. The presence of an identical sequence of amino acids in these four proteins, particularly in association with areas of the molecules that are strongly implicated in catalytic function, is almost too much to attribute to chance alone.

Another example of similarity in sequence is found in the hormones of the pituitary gland whose structures were discussed in Chapters 6 and 7. The formulas for adrenocorticotropic hormone (ACTH) and for two forms of the melanocyte stimulating hormone (MSH) of porcine pituitary tissue are shown in Figure 74 (page 153). The material known as β-MSH contains a heptapeptide sequence which is identical with residues 4 to 10 of ACTH. An even more striking example of recurring sequence is α-MSH, which has a structure identical with the first thirteen residues of ACTH except for the addition of a C-terminal amide group and an N-terminal acyl radical. The similarities in these structures are particularly interesting because of the fact that ACTH is formed in the posterior lobe of the pituitary gland, whereas MSH appears to be synthesized in the *pars intermedia*.

The determination of amino acid sequences in proteins and polypeptides is still at an early stage, and unfortunately we lack sufficient data for a proper statistical analysis of the results. Nevertheless, the data we do have make it tempting to postulate that the "templates" responsible for the biosynthesis of peptide chains involve common sets of "instructions" which correspond to recurring chemical fine structure in the genetic material of the nucleus. Alternatively, various common peptide intermediates that have structures suited to specific functional requirements might be involved in the assembly of different classes of proteins. These hypotheses are attractive from the standpoint of evolutionary theory, which suggests to us a common origin for living things, both present and past and a gradual process of change in variety and kind through the modification of the genotypes available at any moment. This thesis, which is discussed in greater detail in the following chapter, would propose that "primitive" chemical structures having generalized enzymatic or hormonal functions were modified during evolution to yield families of more specialized molecules.

REFERENCES

1. F. S. Sjöstrand and V. Hanzon, *Exptl. Cell Research*, **7**, 393 (1954); *ibid.*, p. 415.
2. M. Swerdlow, A. J. Dalton, and L. S. Birks, *Anal. Chem.*, **28**, 597 (1956).
3. T. Caspersson, *Cell Growth and Cell Function*, Norton, New York, 1950.
4. K. Felix, H. Fischer, and A. Krekels, *Progress in Biophysics*, volume 6, Pergamon Press, London, p. 1, 1956.
5. For a discussion of these, and related studies, see the review by J. Brachet in *The Nucleic Acids*, volume 2 (E. Chargaff and J. N. Davidson, editors), Academic Press, New York, 1955.
6. K. Moldave and C. Heidelberger, *J. Am. Chem. Soc.*, **76**, 679 (1954).
7. R. McMaster-Kaye and H. J. Taylor, *J. Biophys. Biochem. Cytology*, **4**, 5

(1958). (The reader should be cautioned that a direct relationship between nuclear and cytoplasmic RNA is far from established—see for example, J. W. Woodward, *J. Biophys. Biochem. Cytology*, **4**, 383 (1958).

8. Reviewed in a series of papers in *Proc. Nat. Acad. Sci. U.S.*, **44**, No. 2 (1958).
9. P. C. Zamecnik and E. B. Keller, *J. Biol. Chem.*, **209**, 337 (1954).
10. J. A. Gladner and K. Laki, *J. Am. Chem. Soc.*, **80**, 1263 (1958).
11. R. Loftfield, in *Progress in Biophysics and Biochemistry*, Pergamon Press, London, 1958.
12. S. Spiegelman in *The Chemical Basis of Heredity* (W. D. McElroy and B. Glass, editors), Johns Hopkins Press, Baltimore, 1957.
13. J. L. Simkin and T. S. Work, *Nature*, **179**, 1214 (1957).
14. D. Steinberg, M. Vaughan, and C. B. Anfinsen, *Science*, **124**, 389 (1956).

chapter 11

GENES, PROTEINS,
AND
EVOLUTION

" . . . we must remember that heredity, development,
and evolution are essentially epigenetic and not preformistic.
We do not inherit from our ancestors, close or remote,
separate characters, functional or vestigial.   What we do
inherit is, instead, genes which determine the pattern of
developmental processes. . . . "

T. DOBZHANSKY, *Evolution, Genetics, and Man.*

As the genes of a species are modified and reshuf-
fled, occasional organisms will appear within a restricted population
having phenotypic characteristics that enable them to explore desir-
able ecological niches which were unattainable by their predecessors.
The individual changes are generally quite small.   Many generations
must come and go, during which forays into formerly forbidden ter-
ritory by this developing branch of the population become more fre-

quent and are of longer duration as the result of further reorganization of the gene pool by random mutation and natural selection. In time the summation of these changes results in a new species, fully at home in its new environment and sufficiently different in physiology from its distant ancestors that cross-fertilization is no longer possible.

We have discussed, in several earlier chapters, the techniques used by the geneticist for the analysis and description of limited portions of such a chain of events. As long as crosses can be made between different family lines, phenotypic changes can generally be related to specific genes and the spread of these genes through a population can be fairly accurately mapped. Thus, the basic assumptions of evolutionary theory may be directly tested, and with some precision, when the segment of time under consideration is small, and we are able to describe the process in terms of changes in *genotype*. When we deal with evolution on a larger scale, however, the tools of the geneticist are no longer applicable. The evolutionist must now rely on the study of relative morphology and ecology as deduced from the fossil record, or on the comparative anatomy and physiology of living representatives of surviving species.

The principal aim of this book has been to examine the basic principles underlying another possible method for the study of evolution. This method is based on the hypothesis that the individual proteins which characterize a particular species are unique reflections of the genes which control their synthesis. The examination of the chemistry of a series of homologous proteins is, of course, a purely phenotypic approach to the problem. Nevertheless, the evidence available to us, even at this early date, suggests that the structure of proteins may be a relatively direct expression of gene structure and that comparative protein chemistry may furnish a qualitative view of genotypic differences and similarities. If we accept the general hypothesis, we are led to infer, for example, that the "insulin-determining" genes of the pig and the sperm whale are identical, like the insulins whose structures they determine. Indeed, should several genes be concerned with the synthesis of insulin, the same would also be true for these.

Another interesting potentiality of comparative protein chemistry is that it might permit us to determine whether the same phenotypic characteristic, shown by two completely unrelated organisms, is attributable to *analogous* or to *homologous* genes. For example, both bacteriophage T2 and chicken's eggs contain proteins that have lysozyme activity. The genetic material of both coliphage and chickens must be said to contain information that can direct the formation of

THE MOLECULAR BASIS OF EVOLUTION

proteins with this function. Is it possible that these two organisms contain nearly identical (that is, homologous) stretches of genetic material, or are the genes for lysozyme synthesis, and the lysozymes themselves, entirely different? This would appear to be the sort of question that might be attacked directly by the comparative study of protein structure. As we have already seen, in connection with cytochrome c, ribonuclease, hemoglobin, and other proteins, there is excellent evidence which indicates that many homologous genes *do* appear to have survived happily through long periods of time, some well exceeding the span of the fossil record.

A Biochemical Approach to the Species Problem

The paleontologist, in estimating the rates and directions of evolution, must depend almost entirely on morphological evidence. Even with this relatively crude sort of yardstick, he can begin to distinguish patterns of change such as we discussed in Chapter 1, in connection with the characteristics of tooth structure in the evolving horses. He is limited, however, to the *results* of evolution and can never hope to elucidate the underlying physiological changes that participate to produce new phyla.

Although most of the ancient species disappeared, representatives of almost all the phyla escaped extinction by adapting to their new environments, thus perpetuating large parts of heredity. We have available to us, then, a contemporary sample of the life of the past from which we should be able to deduce a great deal about the factors that were decisive in phylogenesis long ago. The study of "biochemical evolution" has already been of considerable value in the establishment of biological interrelationships. For example, the occurrence of melanocyte-stimulating, oxytocic, and vasopressor hormonal activity in extracts of the neural gland if tunicates furnishes strong evidence in support of the assignment of this subphyllum, the Urochordata, to the direct pathway between the invertebrates (which lack MSH activity) and vertebrates. The presence of both arginine phosphate (an invertebrate phosphagen) and creatine phosphate (the typically vertebrate phosphagen) in tunicates adds additional support to this assignment.

We shall not attempt to discuss here the numerous contributions of this sort that biochemistry has made to evolutionary theory. The reader will find this material summarized in a number of comprehensive essays and books.[1, 2, 3] Our present concern is primarily with

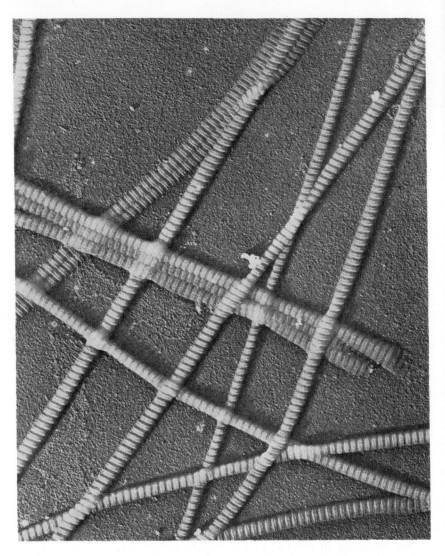

Figure 96. An electron photomicrograph of collagen fibrils from bovine skin. Magnification × 42,000. Obtained through the kindness of Dr. Jerome Gross, Massachusetts General Hospital, Harvard University Medical School.

THE MOLECULAR BASIS OF EVOLUTION

the biochemical changes in protein molecules that are much nearer, in metabolic terms, to the genes themselves than are such products of enzymatic action as the phosphagens, or the eye pigments of *Drosophila*. As Wald has put it "It is a truism in biochemistry that each species of animal and plant possesses specifically different proteins." The full understanding of speciation must, almost certainly, be sought in the structure of proteins. To expand this point a bit, let us consider two elegant examples of speciation that are demonstrably related to changes in protein structure.

The protein collagen is largely responsible for the physical properties of such structural tissues as skin and cartilage. When collagen fibrils (Figure 96) are exposed to heat they change markedly in internal structure and yield the molecular form known as gelatin. Now recent studies by X-ray crystallography have shown that the collagen molecule is very likely composed of three strands of polypeptide, cross-linked through a system of hydrogen bonds of considerable strength.[4] The amino acid sequence, Gly.Pro.Hypro, appears fairly frequently along the chains, and the hydroxyl groups on the hydroxyproline residues are presumably major contributors to the hydrogen bond network. When collagen is heated in solution, the hydrogen bonds become ruptured at a critical temperature, known as the "shrinkage temperature," and the organized structure is quickly disoriented to form the more globular and amorphous gelatin structure. Although the exact mechanism of this rearrangement is not known, it is possible, on the basis of the results of current work on the properties of synthetic polyproline and of mixed polymers of proline and glycine, that the shrinkage may be associated with a *cis-trans* isomerization at proline-proline or proline-hydroxyproline bonds,[5] in conjunction with ordinary "entropic" denaturation.

On the basis of these chemical and physical observations we might suppose that collagen molecules, suited to either cold or warm habitats, could be devised by nature through the introduction or deletion of hydroxyproline residues. Animals living in climates tending to be very warm would do well to utilize collagens with high shrinkage temperatures, and those living in cold climates could do with considerably fewer sites for cross-linkage and with lower shrinkage temperatures.

The studies of K. H. Gustavson and of T. Takahashi on the collagens of fishes suggest that this is precisely the mechanism which has been employed.[6] The shrinkage temperatures of cold-water fishes are always lower than those of warm-water fishes, and an amazingly linear relationship exists between shrinkage temperature and the con-

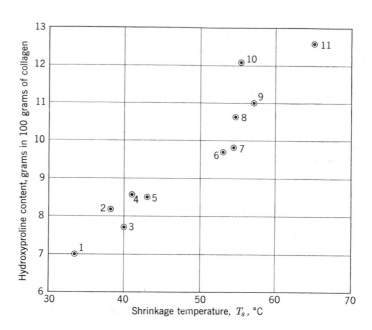

Figure 97. The relationship between the hydroxyproline contents of the collagens of various fishes and their "shrinkage temperature."[6]

tent of hydroxyproline (Figure 97), although the vertebrate collagens are otherwise extremely similar in composition. It is a provocative fact that collagen shrinkage temperatures seem to fall about 15 or 20° above the highest temperatures likely to be encountered by a species, as though this margin of safety were adequate in the ordinary course of climatic events.

The relationship between the visual pigments of marine fishes and the depths of their habitats is another dramatic example of adaptation through modification of protein structure. Denton and Warren,[7] Munz,[8] Wald and his colleagues,[9] and many other investigators have studied the chemical structure and the spectral properties of a variety of fish rhodopsins. Rhodopsin, composed of a vitamin A derivative complexed with a protein, opsin, constitutes the light-sensitive element of the retinal rods. The vitamin A-like prosthetic group, retinene, responsible for light absorption, has been found to be identical in all the species listed in Table 17. Since opsins do not themselves absorb light in the spectral interval between 480 and 503 mμ, the shifts in the position of the absorption maxima shown in Figure 98 must be attributed to the effects of the opsins on the

TABLE 17
Spectral Properties of Rhodopsins from Various Fishes

Species	Summer Range of Depth, fathoms	λ_{max}, mμ	E_{540}/E_{max}
Summer flounder (*Paralichthys dentatus* Linnaeus)	2–10	503	0.695
Scup (*Stenotomus versicolor* Mitchell)	1–20	498	0.586
Butterfish (*Poronotus triacanthus* Peck)	1–30	499	0.610
Barracuda (*Sphyraena borealis* DeKay)	1–10	498	0.575
Cod (*Gadus callarias* Linnaeus)	5–75	496	0.530
Cusk (*Brosme brosme* Müller)	10–100	494	0.455
Lancet-fish (*Alepisarus ferox* Lowe)	>200	480	0.250

spectral properties of retinene. The mechanism by which conjugation with opsin can induce a change in the spectral properties of retinene is quite obscure. We have previously discussed a related instance of a spectral shift, where the absorption characteristics of the

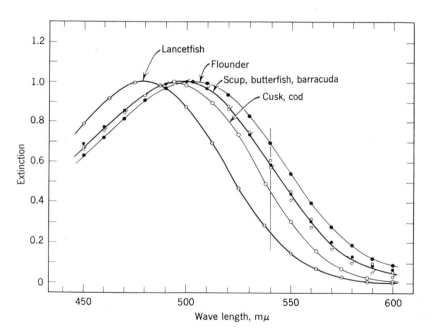

Figure 98. Absorption spectra of rhodopsins of marine fishes in 2 per cent aqueous digitonin solution. The maximum absorption (λ_{max}) shifts toward shorter wavelengths in rough correlation with the depth of habitat. See Table 17.

GENES, PROTEINS, AND EVOLUTION

tyrosine residue are modified by hydrogen bonding of the hydroxyl group. The shift in this case was small, of the order of a few millimicrons. In the rhodopsin absorption system maxima differ by as much as 23 mμ as we move from the summer flounder to the lancet fish. This large shift implies a major change in the nature of the interaction between protein and prosthetic group.

The biological observation that makes all this of special interest is the fact that a correlation is observed between the mean depth of habitat of the various species of fishes and the spectral properties of their visual pigments. The correlation is not at all exact and, as the data in Table 17 show, a wide spread of λ_{max} exists at all depths. Nevertheless, the information available is sufficient to form the basis of a strong hypothesis. Over twenty years ago G. L. Clarke observed that the increasing blueness of light with depth in the ocean raises "the question of the possibility of a shift in the sensitivity of the eye of a deep-water fish toward the blue end of the spectrum." This possibility is realized in the spectroscopic observations just listed, and it is now possible to apply the techniques of protein chemistry to the elucidation of the details of this fascinating chapter in biochemical ecology. The study of the structural modifications in opsin which have taken place during the evolution of the fishes will be especially interesting since, as we have seen for the insulins and cytochromes c, large spans of evolutionary time may pass without too extensive a change in a particular protein molecule. The changes in the opsin molecule may be so cleverly contrived and so incisive that extensive alterations in sequence and folding have been unnecessary. On the other hand, if alterations *have* been extensive, we shall be required to rationalize a very complex set of interactions between protein and prosthetic group. Both alternatives are intriguing, to say the least, and the study of the chemistry of the opsins should make a most valuable contribution to the understanding of evolution at the molecular level.

The Rate of Evolution

As G. G. Simpson has pointed out, the question "How fast has evolution occurred?" is meaningless without the addition of the qualifications, "the evolution of what organisms, of which of their structures, and at what time in their history." The opossum, for example, has changed relatively little in the past 80,000,000 years, whereas the evolution of the horses during the past 60,000,000 years has involved at least eight distinct genera.

Just as the anatomical organization of some organisms has changed much more rapidly than that of others, it seems likely that we shall find a large spread in the rates at which specific protein molecules have been modified during evolution. Although our basis for discussion of this point is still very thin, it is already evident that some proteins have undergone far greater structural change than others over an equivalent period. Compare, for example, the somatotropins of the sperm whale and the sheep with the insulins of these same species. Although the changes in insulin structure have been restricted to very minor modifications in a limited part of one polypeptide chain, the somatotropins are quite markedly modified in molecular weight, in cystine content, and in the number of polypeptide chains. Equally striking differences in degrees of modification exist between numerous others of the examples discussed in Chapter 7.

How are we to plan our experimental approach in attempting to establish some chemical coherence in the tremendous puzzle of speciation? We must, it would seem to me, begin with the basic assumption that the phenotypic character of a species is primarily determined by its unique spectrum of proteins. We may then proceed to a study of the extent to which each of the individual proteins within any spectrum may be modified without loss of biological function. As we already know, the degree of "violability" of different proteins may vary enormously as judged from the results of *in vitro* studies on denaturation and chemical modification in relation to function. Even here, however, many of the observed differences in sensitivity may be overemphasized and may depend on the choice of methods used for modification. Even though two proteins may be very similar in regard to the proportion of their total structure that is essential for function, one set of reagents may attack critical parts of one and not seriously alter the other. Amino groups, for example, may be acetylated with essentially no effect in pepsin, but at least some of these same groups appear to be critical for the activity of lysozyme. A proper comparison of two biologically active proteins thus must depend on the use of a wide variety of inactivating reagents, and ultimately on the deliberate degradative sort of study that aims to reduce proteins to their minimum, functionally adequate size.

Since, however, proteins *can* be modified without loss of function, it seems certain that the permissible degree of modification, in terms of fractions of their total structure, will vary somewhat from molecular species to species. It does not seem too farfetched to think of the proteins of a given organism as being subdivisible into those that have structures quite closely tailored to an essential functional requirement, those that are designed with only moderate "efficiency" or whose function is relatively dispensable, and those that are intermediate. Once again, illustrations come to mind. Several individuals exhibiting only slight clinical abnormality have been shown to be *completely* devoid of serum albumin. These individuals, able to lead a normal existence, are living evidence for the dispensability of this protein under the ecological circumstances peculiar to humans. On the other hand, no one will question the inability of most species to survive in the absence of cytochrome c or of the enzymes necessary for oxidative phosphorylation.

If we accept these subdivisions of the protein spectrum, we may "express" a species in terms of a hierarchy of protein structures ranging in violability from none to very much. The further evolution of this species, involving the usual mutation and natural selection, would then be reflected in a change in its proteins, one end of the spectrum remaining relatively fixed while the other may change considerably. Thus the cytochrome c molecule, which we might think of as a relatively "primitive" protein, and indispensable for most life, would be stubbornly perpetuated in the evolving phyla with minimal change, whereas the structure of the serum albumins might fluctuate with the shifting parameters of natural selection. From time to time, entirely new protein structures might arise, as in the dramatic appearance of insulin and of other hormones at the point in evolution when the protovertebrates and vertebrates appeared. The molecular basis for such "explosive" appearance of new protein entities is, of course, completely obscure. Only a thorough understanding of the processes of protein biosynthesis and of genetic information transfer will enable us to choose between such alternatives as the *de novo* creation of a whole new gene as opposed to the fortuitous reshuffling of already available genetic units.

We may safely predict that the patterns of change observed in the protein spectrum by future biochemists will not always be smooth and tidy. The criteria of natural selection will differ greatly from species to species, from environment to environment, and from period to period, and the survival value of gene mutations in a population, and of their images in the phenotype, will be quite varied.

A large number of important aspects of evolution have been omitted from this book. Some of these omissions may be attributed to type-

THE MOLECULAR BASIS OF EVOLUTION

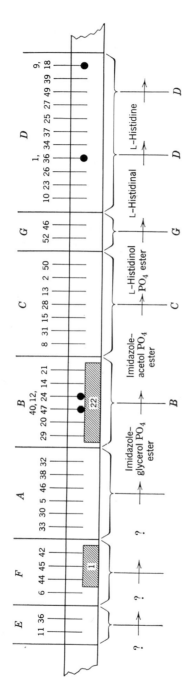

Figure 99. Linkage map of the region of the chromosome of *Salmonella typhimurium* which controls the stepwise synthesis of histidine. The enzymes which catalyze the series of reactions shown at the bottom of the figure are presumably synthesized under the control of various "cistrons" labeled *E, F, A, B, C, G,* and *D.* The order of the individual mutations within any cistron is only tentative. These mutations were mapped by use of the "transduction" technique described in Chapter 4. These fascinating results suggest that in *Salmonella* the cistrons corresponding to the biosynthetic enzymes are arranged in the same order as the biosynthetic steps themselves. For details consult the review by Philip E. Hartman in *The Chemical Basis of Heredity,* Johns Hopkins Press, 1957.

writer fatigue. Most of them, however, have been purposely omitted because of the lack of adequate factual material for discussion, and this book is already well supplied with speculation. We might, for example, have taken up the question of the spatial organization of genes in relation to function. The recent studies on the mapping of genes related to histidine biosynthesis in *Salmonella* (Figure 99) by Hartmann, Demerec, and others indicate that the various cistrons associated with the series of intermediate enzymes occur in the same region of the genetic strand and that these genetic determinants are arranged on the gene map *in the same order as the reaction sequence itself.* A schematic representation of this linkage map is given in Figure 99. The evolutionary implication that linked biochemical steps have been added, successively, in sequence along the chromosome is a very exciting one but is clearly not general. In *Neurospora*, for example, genetic loci for closely related enzymatic steps are scattered at random throughout the chromosomal apparatus.

We might, also, have spent some time on the question of cytoplasmic heredity, which we know to be of importance in many biological systems. Here again the scarcity of published information is a limiting factor. The study of inheritance of traits in a non-Mendelian fashion is likely to be difficult and confusing, and the genetic or biochemical study of such traits might receive disproportionately little attention. As Nanney has recently suggested, "It is perhaps only natural that investigations of 'messy' characteristics are discontinued before publication and that investigators move on to traits more readily analyzed." The omnivorous reader will find Nanney's review[10] of the subject of cytoplasmic heredity in *The Chemical Basis of Heredity* excellent reading.

The list of omissions can be extended. The chemistry of RNA and its genetic properties, the rearrangements of genes within the chromosome and the phenotypic consequences of such rearrangements, the problem of polyploidy, the interactions of nonallelic genes—many of these might, even now, be discussed with some intelligence in biochemical terms.

The relationships between genotype and phenotype will, predictably, become a major preoccupation of more and more "pure" and medical scientists during the coming years. This book has grown out of my own attempts to arrive at some sort of appreciation of the potentialities of chemical genetics and the evolutionary approach. It will have been well worth the effort if it can help to stimulate the growing interest in evolution as the central theme in the life sciences.

REFERENCES

1. J. B. S. Haldane, *The Biochemistry of Genetics*, Allen & Unwin, London, second impression 1956.
2. M. Florkin, *Biochemical Evolution*, Academic Press, New York, 1949.
3. G. Wald, in *Modern Trends in Physiology and Biochemistry*, Academic Press, New York, 1952.
4. A. Rich and F. H. C. Crick, *Nature*, **176**, 915 (1955).
5. W. F. Harrington, *Nature*, **181**, 997 (1958).
6. K. H. Gustavson, *The Chemistry and Reactivity of Collagen*, Academic Press, New York, 1956. The analytical studies of Takahashi are discussed on pages 224–227.
7. E. J. Denton and F. J. Warren, *Nature*, **178**, 1059 (1956).
8. F. W. Munz, *Science*, **125**, 1142 (1957).
9. G. Wald, P. K. Brown and P. S. Brown, *Nature*, **180**, 969 (1957).
10. D. L. Nanney, *The Chemical Basis of Heredity* (W. D. McElroy and B. Glass, editors), Johns Hopkins Press, Baltimore, 1957.

INDEX

Differentiation, of teeth, 10
  reptilian jaw, 13
Di-isopropylfluorophosphate, 208
Dinitrophenylation, 106, 107
Diploid cells, 21
Disulfide bridges, location of in pro-
  teins, 113, 114

Élan vital, 6, 13
Endoplasmic reticulum, 196, 197, 199
Entelechy, 6, 13
Enzymatic digestion of polypeptide
  chains, 106–111, 113
Ergastoplasm, 196
Evolution, rate of, 218

"Fingerprinting" technique for peptides, 144

Gamete, 21
Genes, 15, 16
  analogous, 142
  determinants of protein structure,
    164
  dominant, 16
  homologous, 142
  linked, 22, 23
  molecular size of, 27, 28
  recessive, 16
  substructure of, 67
Genetic codes, 62–65
Genetic fine structure, 173
Genetic maps, 24, 25, 26
  fine structure, 86, 88–95, 173
  in bacteriophage, 84, 173–176
Genetic recombination, 16
Genetics of host range in bacteriophage, 173
Genotype, 15
Growth hormones, species differences
  in, 158
Gryphaea, evolution of, 7–10

Haploid cells, 21
α-Helical coiling in globular proteins,
  118, 119
Helical coiling in proteins, 100, 101
α-Helix, 100–102
  dimensions of, 101

Hemoglobins, 167–171
  abnormal, structural differences in,
    169–171
  species differences in, 158, 160, 161
Heredity, cytoplasmic, 222
Heterozygote, 16
Homozygote, 16
Horses, evolution of, 10–12
Host range genetics in bacteriophage,
  173
Hypertensins, species differences in,
  155, 157

Immunochemical comparisons of serum
  proteins, 162, 163
Independent assortment, law of, 18, 19
Insulin, active degradation product of,
  128
  structure of, 122
Insulins, species difference in, 154, 155

Law of independent assortment, 18, 19
Law of segregation, 16, 17
Linkage, 22, 23
Linkage groups, 23, 26
Linkage map, for histidine biosynthesis
  in *Salmonella*, 221, 222
  of T4 bacteriophage, 90, 92
Lozenge genes, 28, 29
Lysozyme, of bacteriophage, 73–75,
  183, 212
  specificity of, 74

Macroevolution, 7, 9, 10
Maps, genetic, in bacteriophage, 84,
  173–176
Megaevolution, 7, 9,
Meiosis, 19, 21, 22
  stages in, 22
Melanotropins, species differences in,
  154
  structures of, 153
Membrane, cytoplasmic, 196–199
Mendelian genetics, 16–19
Microevolution, 7
"Microheterogeneity," 187
Mitosis, 19, 20
  stages in, 20
Mutagenesis, chemical, 40
Mutants, deletion, 86, 89, 91
Mutation, 27